PROJECT 18 Menu Makeovers

A Playbook for Healthy Eating

at St.Vincent

**Lori Walton, RN BSN &
Gretchen Fisher, RD CD**

Foreword by
Peyton Manning

WP Winters Publishing
winterspublishing.com
812-663-4948

Menu Makeovers
A Playbook for Healthy Eating

Photography:
Photos on pages 8, 11, 12, 30, 35, 36, 38, 49, 50, 90, 93, 94, 96, 98,
    101, 103, 105, 134, 140, 141, 152, 154, 157 and 160 courtesy of polinaosherov.com
Photos on pages 17, 41 and 174 courtesy of Rachel Winters
Other photos courtesy of iStock Photos
Cover Concept and Text Page Concept: Kate Malone
Cover and Text Page Design: Rachel Winters

ISBN 10 - 1-883651-38-7
ISBN 13 - 978-1-883651-38-1
Library of Congress Control Number: 2010926496

Printed in China

Published by:
Winters Publishing
P.O. Box 501
Greensburg, IN 47240
812-663-4948
winterspublishing.com

Dedications

I would like to thank my family for their patience, love, support, and for enduring endless taste testing of multiple batches of recipes that went into making this book. I would also like to thank Gretchen Fisher, RD, whose hard work and expertise made completing this book possible. I would like to dedicate this book to them, to all the families in the L.I.F.E. for Kids program who make my work so rewarding, and to all of us who have ever struggled with being overweight and trying to be healthy in our often unhealthy world.

Stay Strong!

Lori

I would like to thank my parents, Gert and Jeff Fisher, and my three brothers, Greg, Jerry, and Jason Fisher, for all their love, encouragement and support over the years. I love all of you so much and dedicate this cookbook in your honor. I wish all of our L.I.F.E. for Kids families the best, as they begin their journey toward a healthier lifestyle. Their hard work and dedication throughout this program is truly inspiring, and I find nothing more rewarding than to be a part of their journey.

Bon appétit!

Gretchen

Acknowledgements

The assistance of the following
individuals and companies helped make
it possible to publish this book.
We offer our thanks to:

Polina Osherov, for taking many of the
photographs shown on the recipe pages

Sodexo, for providing and preparing the food
used in many of the photographs

Marsh Supermarkets, for their
ongoing support of Project 18

Peyton Manning Children's Hospital at St.Vincent

St.Vincent Health

Table of Contents

Foreword

Getting fit is not something that happens overnight, or even something that is really ever finished. For athletes like me, staying fit and healthy is a full time job. Setting goals, eating smarter and being active are the keys to getting started and maintaining a healthy lifestyle.

Healthy eating can be a tricky thing, and it doesn't mean you can never eat the not so healthy foods you love. *Menu Makeovers* is a cookbook designed to promote healthy eating while still enabling you to eat the foods you love at home. I hope you enjoy the recipes provided here and have a good time cooking with your parents. Remember, if you start with a balanced diet, you can have your cake and eat it too - as long as you are eating the foods that keep you fit and healthy.

As you start your plan towards a healthier lifestyle, please join me in taking the Project 18 Pledge.

I, ... , pledge to try my best to live healthy. I will spend an hour of every day doing something fun and active, like playing basketball, riding bikes and other activities. I will try to eat a balanced diet with a variety of fruits and vegetables every day. I will avoid sugary drinks and sugary snacks on a regular basis. I will spend two hours or less each day watching TV and playing computer or video games. And I will keep a positive attitude, even when times are tough.

. . . .
My signature

. . . .
Signature of parent(s)

Peyton 18 Manning

. . . .
Peyton Manning's signature

8

Fast Food Breakfast

McDonald's® Menu Makeover

	McDonald's® Breakfast Sausage McMuffin® with Egg, Hash Browns, Medium Orange Juice	McDonald's® Better Choice Egg McMuffin®, Apple Dippers, 1% Low Fat Milk Jug	Menu Makeover Better Breakfast Muffin, Rockin' Round Browns, Skim Milk (8 oz)
Calories	780	440	359
Total Fat	36g	15g	4.5g
Sat. Fat	11.5g	6g	0g
Fiber	4g	2g	12.6g
Sugar	39g	21g	13.3g
Protein	22g	26g	33.1g

Better Breakfast Muffin

	McDonald's® Sausage McMuffin® with Egg	Better Breakfast Muffin
Calories	450	220
Total Fat	27g	4.5g
Sat. Fat	10g	0g
Fiber	2g	10g
Sugar	2g	1.3g
Protein	21g	22.7g

Better Breakfast Muffin

Ingredients:

- 1 Thomas® Light Multigrain English muffin
- ¼ cup egg substitute
- 1 Morningstar Farms® soy sausage patty
- 1 slice Kraft® fat free cheese

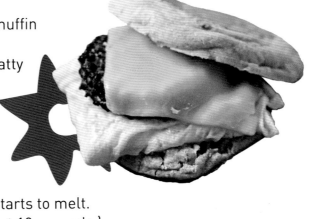

Directions:

1: Cook sausage patty as directed.
2: Cook egg substitute as directed.
3: Toast English muffin.
4: Put cheese on top of sausage until it starts to melt.
   (You may need to microwave it for about 10 seconds.)
5: Put sausage, egg and cheese on English muffin, and enjoy!

Makes 1 serving.

*Lighten Up: Leave off the sausage.

*Switch It Up: You can substitute the soy sausage for turkey sausage (from white meat only), Canadian bacon, ham or turkey bacon.

*Nutrition Boost: Chop in some green peppers or tomato into egg substitute, or add some salsa.

*Quick Fix: Buy Jimmy Dean's® frozen breakfast D-lights sandwiches made with turkey sausage, egg whites and cheese.

Rockin' Round Browns

	McDonald's® Hash Browns 1 patty (2 oz)	Rockin' Round Browns (1 serving)
Calories	150	59
Total Fat	9g	0g
Sat. Fat	1.5g	0g
Fiber	2g	2.6g
Sugar	0g	0g
Protein	1g	2.4g

Rockin' Round Browns

Ingredients:
- 2 ½ cups frozen shredded potatoes
- 1 ½ cups thinly diced onions
- 1 teaspoon salt
- Nonfat spray oil
- I Can't Believe It's Not Butter® pump spray

Directions:
1: Preheat oven to 425°.
2: In a large bowl, mix all ingredients together, except spray oil and spray butter.
3: Spray a cookie sheet with nonfat spray oil.
4: Divide mixture into four mounds and place on the cookie sheet.
5: Top with a couple of sprays of spray butter.
6: Roast for 15 minutes, then turn mounds over with spatula, pressing down to flatten to 4-inch diameter rounds (cakes will still be soft). Reduce oven temperature to 350°. Bake until cakes are golden and crisp around edges, for about 45 minutes longer.

Makes 4 servings.

*Lighten Up: Replace half the shredded potatoes with shredded zucchini. Be sure to squeeze shredded zucchini squash with a paper towel, to drain out as much water as you can. This will make it crispier!

*Switch It Up: Mix in ¼ cup Parmesan cheese or 2% shredded cheddar cheese. This does increase the calories to 87 per serving.

*Nutrition Boost: Throw in some diced red and green peppers, or use sweet potatoes in place of regular potatoes.

*Quick Fix: Use frozen potato patties, and bake in the oven according to directions.

Starbucks® Menu Makeover

	Starbucks® Breakfast White Chocolate Mocha Frappuccino® (made with whole milk and whipped cream), Cinnamon Roll	Starbucks® Better Choice White Chocolate Mocha Frappuccino® (light blended), Pumpkin Loaf	Menu Makeover Winning White Chocolate Frap, Super Cinnamon Rolls
Calories	990	570	378
Total Fat	42g	17g	3.4g
Sat. Fat	26g	3.5g	1.3g
Fiber	3g	5g	6.3g
Sugar	93g	63g	48g
Protein	22g	12g	11g

Winning White Chocolate Frap

	Starbucks® White Chocolate Mocha Frappuccino® (16 oz made with whole milk and whipped cream)	Winning White Chocolate Frap (16 oz)
Calories	500	138
Total Fat	22g	2g
Sat. Fat	14g	1.3g
Fiber	0g	5.3g
Sugar	59g	20g
Protein	15g	5g

Winning White Chocolate Frap

Ingredients:
- 1 cup cold, strong coffee
- ½ cup skim milk, light soy milk or unsweetened almond milk
- 2 tablespoons white chocolate sugar free syrup (found in coffee aisle of grocery store)
- 3 packets Splenda®
- 2 cups fat free chocolate ice cream or frozen yogurt
- 1 cup crushed ice

Directions:
1: Place coffee, milk, syrup and Splenda® in blender and blend until mixed.
2: Mix in ice cream and ice. Blend until smooth.

Optional: For only 20 more calories, top with 2 tablespoons Cool Whip Free®, and sprinkle with one teaspoon cocoa powder.

Makes 3 servings.

*Lighten Up: Replace 1 cup frozen yogurt with 2 tablespoons chilled chocolate pudding and 4 ice cubes (or more until desired consistency).

*Switch It Up: Throw in a small handful of Teddy Grahams®, a 100-calorie Oreo® Crisps package, or a handful of chocolate dried cereal such as Coco Puffs®.

*Nutrition Boost: Increase the fiber by blending in one frozen or chilled banana.

*Quick Fix: Mix together 2 cups fat free or low fat coffee ice cream, 1 cup skim milk, 2 tablespoons white chocolate sugar free syrup, and 1 tablespoon reduced sugar chocolate syrup.

Super Cinnamon Rolls

Roll Ingredients:

- 6 English muffins
- I Can't Believe It's Not Butter® pump spray
- 12 tablespoons (¾ cup) evaporated skim milk
- ⅔ cup packed brown sugar
- 1 teaspoon cinnamon/sugar seasoning

Directions:

1: Flour cutting board, rolling pin and muffin tray.
2: Open each muffin and lay on floured board with inside facing up. Roll muffin halves flat with rolling pin. Slightly overlap ends of 2 muffin halves.
3: Spray each muffin (2 halves) with 4-5 sprays of spray butter.
4: Spread 1 tablespoon evaporated skim milk over each muffin.
5: Mix brown sugar and cinnamon/sugar seasoning well.
6: Spread 1 tablespoon brown sugar/seasoning mixture over each muffin.
7: Carefully roll up each muffin, and curve into muffin tin, holding sideways, so a nice top edge is showing.
8: Top each with 1 teaspoon brown sugar/seasoning mixture.
9: Spray each with 2-3 sprays of butter, then top with 1 more tablespoon evaporated skim milk.
10: Bake at 350° for 25 minutes.

Icing Ingredients:

- ¼ cup fat free cream cheese
- ¼ cup skim milk
- ¼ cup powdered sugar
- 1 teaspoon vanilla extract

Directions:

1: Combine cream cheese and powdered sugar. Gradually whisk in milk and vanilla, and mix until soft and well blended.
2: Spread evenly over baked rolls, while they are still warm.

Makes 6 cinnamon rolls.

*Lighten Up: Substitute sugar with Splenda®.

*Switch It Up: Add 1 tablespoon orange peel to icing.

*Nutrition Boost: Top rolls with nuts, Kashi® GOLEAN Crunch!® cereal, or flax seed. Nuts and flax seed are high in protein, fiber, and omega-3 fatty acids, which are shown to help keep the heart strong and reduce the risk of dementia.

*Quick Fix: Use a frozen pre-made bread dough loaf in place of the English muffins.

Super Cinnamon Rolls

	Starbucks® Cinnamon Roll	Super Cinnamon Rolls (1 roll)
Calories	490	240
Total Fat	20g	1.4g
Sat. Fat	12g	0g
Fiber	3g	1g
Sugar	34g	28g
Protein	7g	6g

Krispy Kreme® Menu Makeover

	Krispy Kreme® Breakfast 1 Donut Hole, 1 Apple Fritter, 1 Chocolate Glazed Donut, Lemon Sherbet Kreme Chiller	Krispy Kreme® Better Choice 1 Original Glazed Donut, 1 Original Cinnamon Glazed Donut, 1 Pumpkin Spice Cake Donut Hole, Water	Menu Makeover Holey Moley Donut Holes, Apple Fritter Flip Flops, I'm No Ding Dong Donuts, Tootie Fruity Sherbet Smoothie
Calories	1310	462	479
Total Fat	62.7g	26.7g	8.4g
Sat. Fat	41.7g	13.2g	4.9g
Fiber	2g	0g	7.1g
Sugar	108.7g	25.7g	48.7g
Protein	14.5g	4.5g	20.4g

Holey Moley Donut Holes

	Krispy Kreme® Donut Hole	Holey Moley Donut Holes (1 donut hole)
Calories	50	30
Total Fat	2.7g	0.8g
Sat. Fat	1.2g	0.4g
Fiber	0g	0g
Sugar	3.7g	3.3g
Protein	0.5g	0.4g

Holey Moley Donut Holes

Donut Ingredients:
- 1 refrigerated package reduced fat crescent roll dough
- Nonfat cooking spray

Icing Ingredients:
- 1 cup powdered sugar
- 2 tablespoons skim milk
- ¼ teaspoon lemon juice
- ¼ teaspoon vanilla extract

Directions:
1: Preheat oven to 375°.
2: Open refrigerated dough and separate the 8 precut pieces of crescent dough.
3: Take 1 roll and pull the dough apart into 5 even pieces. Roll the pieces into balls. Repeat for the other 7 rolls, until you have 40 donut holes. Spray cookie sheet.
4: Place donut holes onto sprayed cookie sheet and bake for 7 minutes, or until the bottom of dough starts to slightly turn light brown.
5: While dough is cooking, prepare icing by mixing all the icing ingredients together in a small bowl.
6: Once donut holes are ready, dip each one into the glaze and enjoy!

Makes 40 donut holes.

*Lighten Up: Serve donut holes with a side of diced fresh fruit or applesauce. The more food groups you have on your plate, the less likely you will be to overeat.

*Switch It Up: Roll donuts in sprinkles, coconut, or crushed nuts.

*Nutrition Boost: Boost up your breakfast and help build strong bones by adding an 8-ounce glass of skim milk. According to the National Dairy Council, 7 out of 10 boys and 9 out of 10 girls are not meeting their calcium needs.

*Quick Fix: Skip the icing and roll donut holes in powdered sugar.

Apple Fritter Flip Flops

Fritter Ingredients:

- 1 package Pillsbury® hot roll mix
- 1 cup hot water
- 2 tablespoons Smart Balance® stick margarine
- 1 egg
- ¼ cup sugar
- ½ teaspoon nutmeg

- 1 tablespoon cinnamon
- ½ teaspoon ginger
- 1 tablespoon apple pie spice
- 2 large apples, chopped (about 2 cups)
- Nonfat cooking spray

Icing Ingredients:

- 1 cup powdered sugar
- 1 tablespoon reduced calorie maple syrup
- 2 tablespoons skim milk

Directions:

1: Preheat oven to 375°. Combine contents of hot roll mix box and yeast packet in large bowl; mix well.
2: Stir in hot water, margarine and egg until dough pulls away from sides of bowl. Turn dough out onto lightly floured surface. With greased or floured hands, shape dough into a ball.
3: Knead dough for 5 minutes until smooth. To knead, fold dough over towards you; press down and away with heels of hands. Rotate dough a quarter turn; continue kneading. Dough should be fairly sticky. If overly sticky, sprinkle flour over hands. Too much flour will result in hard, dry fritters.
4: Mix together sugar, nutmeg, cinnamon, ginger and apple pie spice with apples. Fold apple mixture into dough.
5: Cover dough with large bowl or towel, and let rest for 5 minutes.
6: Separate dough into 15 pieces and place on a sprayed cookie sheet.
7: Bake for 20 to 30 minutes or until bottom slightly turns light brown.
8: Mix icing ingredients together. Dip baked, warm fritters into icing and enjoy.

Makes 15 fritters.

*Lighten Up: Leave out the Smart Balance® stick margarine, and add 2 tablespoons applesauce.

*Switch It Up: Replace apples with diced peaches, berries, or your favorite type of fruit.

*Nutrition Boost: Leave the apple peel on. Not only does the apple peel provide a great source of fiber, it also contains something called triterpenoids - a compound that has been shown in research studies to inhibit or kill cancer.

*Quick Fix: Use refrigerated low fat crescent roll dough, instead of using the hot roll mix. Unroll crescent roll dough and place in a sprayed pan. Top dough with chopped apples, and bake at 375° until dough becomes light brown.

Apple Fritter Flip Flops

	Krispy Kreme® Apple Fritter	Apple Fritter Flip Flops (1 fritter)
Calories	380	174
Total Fat	20g	3.8g
Sat. Fat	10g	1.4g
Fiber	2g	1.1g
Sugar	24g	11.9g
Protein	4g	4.5g

I'm No Ding Dong Donuts

Donut Ingredients:

- 2 tablespoons margarine or butter
- ½ cup sugar
- ¼ cup brown sugar
- ¾ cup potato flakes
- ¾ cup water
- ¼ cup Egg Beaters®
- 2 tablespoons unsweetened applesauce
- ½ cup sour milk (½ tablespoon vinegar to ½ cup milk)
- 2 cups flour
- ½ cup wheat flour
- 1 teaspoon baking soda
- 2 teaspoons baking powder
- 1 teaspoon nutmeg
- ½ teaspoon salt
- 1 teaspoon vanilla extract

Chocolate Icing Ingredients:

- 1 cup powdered sugar
- ⅓ cup cocoa powder
- 2 ½ tablespoons soy milk (or less, depending on desired thickness)

Directions:

1: In a large bowl, cream together the butter and sugars.
2: Beat in potato flakes, water, Egg Beaters®, applesauce and milk.
3: In a separate bowl, mix flours, baking soda, baking powder, nutmeg and salt. Add wet ingredients and vanilla, and mix until combined.
4: Cover and place in refrigerator for 1 hour.
5: Roll out dough ½-inch thick on a floured surface, and cut out donuts. Place on a lightly greased cookie sheet, and bake at 400° for 10 minutes.
6: While dough is cooking, prepare icing by mixing ingredients in a bowl until smooth.
7: When donuts are cool, top with icing and enjoy!

Makes 24 donuts.

*Lighten Up: Top donuts with sugar free chocolate pudding.

*Switch It Up: Use a sugar glaze topping, and roll in sprinkles or nuts.

*Nutrition Boost: Replace the potato flakes and water with ¾ cup pumpkin or sweet potatoes. This will produce a denser donut, packed full of beneficial vitamins and minerals. The bright orange color of these vegetables is a clue that they are rich in beta-carotene - a compound that turns into vitamin A. Beta-carotene helps prevent night blindness, other eye problems, and skin disorders, enhances immunity, and protects against toxins, cancer formations, colds, flu and infections. It is an antioxidant and protector of the cells, while slowing the aging process.

*Quick Fix: Use refrigerated low fat crescent roll dough, and shape into donut.

I'm No Ding Dong Donuts

	Krispy Kreme® Chocolate Donut	I'm No Ding Dong Donuts (1 donut)
Calories	250	107
Total Fat	12g	1.3g
Sat. Fat	6g	0.7g
Fiber	0g	1g
Sugar	10g	9.1g
Protein	2g	2.2g

Tootie Fruity Sherbet Smoothie

	Krispy Kreme® Lemon Sherbet Kreme Chiller (12 oz)	Tootie Fruity Sherbet Smoothie (12 oz)
Calories	630	168
Total Fat	28g	2.5g
Sat. Fat	24g	1.4g
Fiber	0g	5g
Sugar	71g	24.4g
Protein	8g	3.3g

Tootie Fruity Sherbet Smoothie

Ingredients:
- 1 cup sherbet
- ½ cup vanilla nonfat frozen yogurt
- 6 ounces Dannon® Light & Fit® pineapple coconut yogurt (or flavor of your choice)
- 1 cup frozen strawberries
- ¼ cup frozen mango

Directions:
1: Mix all ingredients in a blender until smooth.
2: Serve and enjoy.

Makes 3 (12-ounce) servings.

*Lighten Up: Replace nonfat frozen yogurt with milk or an additional cup of yogurt.

*Switch It Up: Add 2 tablespoons of shredded coconut.

*Nutrition Boost: Add a tablespoon of wheat germ. Wheat germ contains phytosterols, which have been shown to lower cholesterol and blood pressure, and promote heart health. In addition, wheat germ contains high amounts of vitamin E, an antioxidant that helps protect the body from damaging free radicals. Wheat germ is also a good source of omega-3 fatty acids. Wheat germ is also a good source of fiber, which has many benefits, including improved bowel function. It may also reduce the risk of developing heart disease and diabetes, and prevent weight gain.

*Quick Fix: Freeze an extra batch for later use.

Dunkin' Donuts® Menu Makeover

	Dunkin' Donuts® Breakfast Blueberry Muffin, Medium White Hot Chocolate	Dunkin' Donuts® Better Choice Apple Spice Cake Donut, Small Hot Chocolate	Menu Makeover Heavenly Hot Chocolate, Better Blueberry Muffins
Calories	850	450	256
Total Fat	29g	18g	0.9g
Sat. Fat	12.5g	11g	0.2g
Fiber	3g	3g	3.9g
Sugar	96g	38g	20.9g
Protein	9g	5g	11.3g

Heavenly Hot Chocolate

	Dunkin' Donuts® Hot Chocolate (14 oz)	Heavenly Hot Chocolate (14 oz)
Calories	340	133
Total Fat	13g	0.5g
Sat. Fat	11g	0.2g
Fiber	0g	1.7g
Sugar	45g	10.5g
Protein	3g	8.2g

Heavenly Hot Chocolate

Ingredients:

- 3 cups nonfat dry milk powder
- 1 cup Splenda® granular
- ½ cup unsweetened cocoa powder
- 1 (3.4-ounce) package fat free, sugar free instant vanilla pudding mix
- ½ teaspoon ground cinnamon
- ¼ teaspoon nutmeg
- 18 large marshmallows

Directions:

1: Mix all ingredients together.
2: Store in airtight container.
3: To prepare 1 serving, mix 1 cup hot water with ¼ cup dry mix.

Makes 18 (8-ounce) servings.

*Lighten Up: Skip the whipped cream or marshmallows, and save 23 calories.

*Switch It Up: For a twist, try a different flavor of pudding.

*Nutrition Boost: Use soy milk or almond milk in place of water. Unsweetened almond milk has only 40 calories for 8 ounces, compared to skim milk, which contains 80 calories, and whole milk, which contains 150 calories. You will also get an extra boost of vitamin E, which can help keep skin healthy.

*Quick Fix: Use sugar free hot cocoa mix, ½ teaspoon vanilla, 1 large marshmallow, and prepare with hot water.

Better Blueberry Muffins

Streusel Topping Ingredients:

- 2 tablespoons all-purpose flour
- ¼ cup oats
- 2 tablespoons Splenda® Granular
- ½ tablespoon brown sugar
- ½ teaspoon cinnamon
- 1 tablespoon unsweetened applesauce

Muffin Ingredients:

- Butter-flavored cooking spray
- 1 cup all-purpose flour
- 1 cup whole wheat flour
- 1 ½ teaspoons baking soda
- ½ teaspoon cinnamon
- ½ teaspoon salt
- 1 tablespoon lemon zest
- ½ cup sugar
- 1 cup skim milk
- ½ cup unsweetened applesauce
- 1 tablespoon apple cider vinegar
- 1 medium banana, mashed
- 1 cup blueberries, fresh or frozen

Directions:

1: Preheat oven to 375°, and lightly spray a muffin tin.
2: For Streusel Topping: Combine all dry ingredients, and mix well. Mix in applesauce; set aside in refrigerator and chill.
3: For Muffins: In medium bowl, combine flours, baking soda, cinnamon, salt and lemon zest.
4: In large bowl, combine sugar, skim milk, applesauce, vinegar and banana. Mix well.
5: Add dry ingredients to wet ingredients, stir until just combined. Don't overstir.
6: Gently fold in the blueberries, using a rubber spatula.
7: Fill muffin tins about two-thirds full. Top muffins with Streusel mixture.
8: Bake until wooden skewer inserted in center comes out clean, for about 22 minutes.
9: Remove from oven and let cool for 5 minutes. After that, remove muffins from tins, and cool on a wire rack.

Makes 14 muffins.

*Lighten Up: Substitute sugar with Splenda® for baking.

*Switch It Up: Use cranberries instead of blueberries; add some grated orange peel.

*Nutrition Boost: Add more blueberries. They are super high in antioxidants and phytochemicals; two compounds that may help slow the aging process and fight cancer.

*Quick Fix: Purchase Weight Watchers® blueberry muffins at the grocery.

Better Blueberry Muffins

	Dunkin' Donuts® Blueberry Muffin	Better Blueberry Muffins (1 muffin)
Calories	510	123
Total Fat	16g	0.4g
Sat. Fat	1.5g	0g
Fiber	3g	2.2g
Sugar	51g	10.4g
Protein	6g	3.1g

Restaurant Breakfast

Beautiful Biscuits,
Gimmie That Gravy,
Happier Home Fries

Bob Evans® Menu Makeover

	Bob Evans® Breakfast 2 Biscuits and Sausage Gravy, Hash Browns, Kid's Orange Juice (11 oz)	Bob Evans® Better Choice Turkey Sausage, Low-cholesterol Eggs, Wheat Toast, Fruit Cup, Unsweetened Iced Tea (11 oz)	Menu Makeover 2 Beautiful Biscuits, Gimmie That Gravy, Happier Home Fries, V8 Diet Splash® Tropical Blend (11 oz)
Calories	957	362	448
Total Fat	43g	7g	7g
Sat. Fat	22g	2g	2g
Fiber	5g	5g	6.7g
Sugar	27g	18g	13.7g
Protein	17g	27g	20.4g

Beautiful Biscuits

	Bob Evans® 1 Buttermilk Biscuit	Beautiful Biscuits (1 biscuit)
Calories	260	130
Total Fat	13g	3g
Sat. Fat	7g	1g
Fiber	1g	1g
Sugar	2g	3.6g
Protein	5g	3.7g

Beautiful Biscuits

Ingredients:

- Cooking oil spray
- ¾ cup low fat buttermilk
- 1 tablespoon canola oil
- 1 cup all-purpose flour
- 1 cup cake flour
- 1 tablespoon sugar
- 1 ½ teaspoons baking powder
- ½ teaspoon baking soda
- ½ teaspoon salt
- 1 ½ teaspoons cold butter, cut into small pieces
- 1 ½ tablespoons fat free milk, for brushing

Directions:

1: Heat oven to 425°.
2: Spray baking sheet with cooking oil spray.
3: In a small bowl, combine buttermilk and oil. Set aside.
4: In a large bowl, whisk together all-purpose flour, cake flour, sugar, baking powder, baking soda and salt.
5: Using a fork or pastry cutter, cut butter into the dry ingredients until crumbly.
6: Make a hole in the center of the dough, and gradually pour in the buttermilk and oil mixture, stirring with a fork, until just combined, but still lumpy.
7: Transfer the dough to a floured surface, and sprinkle with more flour.
8: Lightly knead for 30 seconds, and roll out evenly until about ½-inch thick.
9: Use the top of a drinking glass, and press down on dough to cut into round pieces.
10: Place biscuits on baking sheet.
11: Brush the tops of the biscuits with milk, and bake for 8 to 12 minutes, or until the tops are golden brown.

Makes 10 servings.

*Lighten Up: Replace oil and butter with 2 tablespoons reduced fat mayonnaise.

*Switch It Up: Top biscuits with unsweetened applesauce and spray butter!

*Nutrition Boost: Replace all-purpose flour with whole wheat flour, and throw in ¼ cup wheat bran and an additional 1 tablespoon canola oil.

*Quick Fix: If you're in a hurry for a batch of biscuits, use Pillsbury® reduced fat refrigerated dough, or prepare dough as directed above and freeze for later use.

Gimmie That Gravy

Ingredients:

- ½ cup nonfat evaporated skim milk
- ¼ cup flour
- 1 cup fat free milk
- 4 ounces Gimme Lean® vegetarian sausage
- ¾ teaspoon pork soup base (This can be found in the ethnic section of the grocery store. If you can't find it, just use chicken or beef stock instead. The pork just gives it a little stronger pork flavor.)
- A pinch each of black pepper and sage
- ½ tablespoon Molly McButter® flavoring

Directions:

1: Pour evaporated skim milk into a medium saucepan.
2: Add 2 tablespoons of flour into milk and whisk briskly. Add remaining flour until all flour is blended in.
3: Whisk fat free milk into the evaporated skim milk and flour mixture.
4: Turn stove to medium heat and bring mixture to gentle boil. Whisking constantly, continue to cook for 10 minutes, until gravy thickens.
5: Reduce heat to medium-low and stir in sausage, soup base, black pepper, sage and butter flavoring. Simmer for 5 minutes, and stir often until sausage is cooked.
6: Serve over warm biscuits.

Makes 4 servings.

*Lighten Up: Instead of pouring gravy over biscuits, dish out ¼-cup servings, and lightly dip your biscuits. This will help keep your portions and calorie intake in check!

*Switch It Up: For a tasty twist, add some chopped onions, 2 splashes of hot sauce, a splash of Worcestershire sauce, and ¼ teaspoon nutmeg.

*Nutrition Boost: For a fun way to increase those vegetables, transform this recipe into a breakfast pizza! Double sausage gravy recipe, and spread gravy over prepared pizza crust, such as Boboli®. Next, layer crust with 1 to 2 cups thinly sliced zucchini, mushrooms, tomatoes and green peppers. Scramble 2 cups Egg Beaters® and spread on top of vegetable layer. Finish with a layer of 2% or fat free cheese. Sprinkle pizza with onions, and bake in preheated oven at 400˚ for 10 to 15 minutes.

*Quick Fix: Explore your local grocery store for a low fat brown gravy sauce, such as McCormick® or Southeastern Mills® gravy mix.

Gimmie That Gravy

	Bob Evans® Breakfast Sausage Gravy (6.8 oz)	Gimmie That Gravy (7 oz)
Calories	171	113
Total Fat	11g	0.5g
Sat. Fat	7g	0g
Fiber	0g	1.7g
Sugar	1g	3.7g
Protein	4g	9g

Happier Home Fries

Ingredients:

- ¾ cup chicken or vegetable stock
- 1 small onion, diced
- ½ large (16-ounce) bunch radishes (8 ounces), diced into small cubes (about 2 cups)
- 3 red potatoes, diced into small cubes
- ¼ teaspoon each dried thyme, garlic salt, basil and parsley
- 1 teaspoon sweet paprika (may use regular paprika for a more subtle taste)
- Salt and pepper, to taste
- I Can't Believe It's Not Butter® pump spray

Directions:

1: In a large, nonstick skillet, heat ½ cup stock to boiling.
2: Add all ingredients, except spray butter.
3: Cover and cook over high heat for 10 minutes, or until liquid is absorbed, turning potatoes and radishes occasionally.
4: Reduce heat to medium, and cook uncovered for an additional 10 to 15 minutes, adding stock as needed, until potatoes and radishes are tender and browned. The longer you let it cook between stirrings, the crispier it will be.
5: Top with spray butter, and serve!

Makes 5 servings.

*Lighten Up: Cut out the potatoes, and increase radishes to 16 ounces (or 4 cups).

*Switch It Up: For super tasty and crispy home fries, try our baked version. Preheat oven to 425°. Spray cookie sheet with nonstick spray, and spread potatoes and radishes far apart on pan. Spray the vegetables with nonstick spray. Coat with onion and herb soup mix. Cook in oven for 30 to 40 minutes, until soft and crisp. Halfway through the cooking process, flip radishes and potatoes over to brown the other side, and add chopped onions to the pan.

*Nutrition Boost: Throw in some diced red and green peppers, diced carrots, cubed sweet potatoes, cubed turnips, or even cubed squash!

*Quick Fix: Microwave potatoes and radishes until soft, but slightly undercooked. Spray skillet with nonfat cooking spray, toss onions in, and cook until translucent. Add potatoes and radishes, and cook on medium for 10 to 15 minutes, turning as little as possible, until soft and browned. If radishes are cooked completely, they will have no bite to their taste.

Happier Home Fries

	Bob Evans® Home Fries (5.2 oz)	Happier Home Fries (5.2 oz)
Calories	185	72
Total Fat	6g	0g
Sat. Fat	1g (0g trans)	0g (0g trans)
Fiber	3g	3g
Sugar	14g	2.8g
Protein	3g	3g

Fast Food Lunch

Fast Food Lunch

Page 40
McDonald's®
Menu Makeover Recipes

Champion Chicken
Nuggets,
"Un-fried" Fries

Page 44
Charley's® Grilled Subs
Menu Makeover Recipes

Philly Chicken
"Wrap and Roll,"
Cheesy Cheese
"Un-fried" Fries

Page 48
Burger King®
Menu Makeover Recipes

Blasted Bean Burger,
My-O-My Onion Rings

Page 52
Arby's®
Menu Makeover Recipes

Perfect Pick Pecan
Chicken Salad,
Sassy Seasoned Fries,
Moooocha Mocha Shake

Page 58
Subway®
Menu Makeover Recipes

Tropical Tuna Salad
Spectacular
Seasoned Subs,
Classic Chips,
Original Oatmeal
Supreme Cookies

Page 64
Dairy Queen®
Menu Makeover Recipes

Fresh-R-Fish Sandwich,
"Un-fried" Fries,
Chocolishus
Chocolate Malt

Page 68
Dairy Queen®
Menu Makeover Recipes

Fantastic Fat Free Franks
Chillin' Chili Cheese Fries,
Coolest Cookie 'n
Cream Shake

Page 74
Steak 'n Shake®
Menu Makeover Recipes

Totally Turkey Club Melt,
Beanerific Baked Beans,
Stupendous
Strawberry Shake

Page 80
Chipotle®
Menu Makeover Recipes

Buff Burrito,
Go Green Guacamole &
Classic Chips

Page 84
Qdoba®
Menu Makeover Recipe

No Nonsense Bean
and Cheese Nacho

Page 86
Taco Bell®
Menu Makeover Recipes

Top Taco Salad,
Caramel Apple
Empa-wow-as

McDonald's® Menu Makeover

	McDonald's® Kid's Meal	McDonald's® Better Choice	Menu Makeover
	Chicken McNuggets® (4 piece), Creamy Ranch Sauce, Medium Fries, Small Sprite®	Chicken McNuggets® (4 piece), Tangy Honey Mustard Sauce, Side Salad w/ Newman's Own® Low-fat Italian Dressing, Apple Dippers, 1% Low Fat Milk Jug	Champion Chicken Nuggets, Fat Free Ranch Dressing (2 tbsp), "Un-fried" Fries, 1 Small Apple, Sliced, Dannon® Dan-o-nino (1.76 oz cup)
Calories	890	475	450
Total Fat	46g	19.5g	4.7g
Sat. Fat	7g	3.5g	1.3g
Fiber	5g	1g	20.6g
Sugar	43g	30g	26g
Protein	15g	21g	31.1g

Champion Chicken Nuggets

	McDonald's® Chicken McNuggets® (4 piece)	Champion Chicken Nuggets (4 piece)
Calories	190	152
Total Fat	12g	1.7g
Sat. Fat	2g	0.3g
Fiber	0g	14g
Sugar	0g	0.4g
Protein	10g	21.1g

Champion Chicken Nuggets

Ingredients:
- Canola oil spray
- ¼ cup egg substitute
- ½ cup Fiber One® cereal, ground
- Pinch each of garlic salt, pepper and onion powder
- 2 ounces uncooked chicken breast, cut into nuggets

Directions:
1: Preheat oven to 400°.
2: Spray baking sheet.
3: Pour egg substitute in a small container.
4: Place ground cereal and spices in a plastic resealable food bag.
5: Dip chicken pieces in egg substitute, place into bag, seal, and shake bag to coat chicken.
6: Place chicken on pre-sprayed baking sheet, and bake for 15 minutes or until no pink in center remains.

Makes 1 serving (4 nuggets).

*Creative Idea: Make your own "Happy Meals" at home! Serve with baked fries, carrot or celery sticks, apple slices or mandarin oranges, and dipping sauce, such as fat free honey mustard, ranch, barbecue sauce or ketchup. Don't forget a small toy! Put it all in a decorative brown paper lunch bag or gift bag.

*Lighten Up: Leave off the breading, and marinate chicken with fat free Italian salad dressing.

*Switch It Up: Use cayenne seasoning or ranch powder.

*Nutrition Boost: Use tofu in place of chicken by cutting firm or extra firm tofu into small squares, and bake as directed. Soy contains a compound called isoflavonens shown to be beneficial for the heart.

*Quick Fix: Use frozen vegetable chicken nuggets by Morningstar Farms® or Boca® burger.

"Un-fried" Fries

	McDonald's® Medium French Fries (4.1 oz)	"Un-fried" Fries (4.9 oz)
Calories	380	128
Total Fat	19g	0.2g
Sat. Fat	2.5g	0g
Fiber	5g	3g
Sugar	0g	1.6g
Protein	4g	3.5g

"Un-fried" Fries

Ingredients:

- 1 medium potato
- Olive oil cooking spray
- Salt or seasoning, to taste (optional)

Directions:

1: Wash potato well, and slice into desired size sticks, including the skin.
2: Preheat oven to 450°.
3: Spray baking sheet.
4: Spread potato slices on baking sheet, and spray potatoes with olive oil cooking spray.
5: Bake for about 15 to 20 minutes, until golden brown.
6: Flip potato slices over with a spatula, and continue baking for an additional 10 to 15 minutes, until golden brown.

Makes 1 serving.

*Lighten Up: Use butternut squash in place of regular potatoes.

*Switch It Up: For an alternative flavor, season with seasoning salt, ranch powder, cheese powder, or barbecue powder.

*Nutrition Boost: Use sweet potatoes in place of regular potatoes to get a higher source of vitamins A and C. Sweet potatoes also have a lower glycemic load than white potatoes. This means that the sweet potato has less effect on blood sugar and blood insulin levels than the white potato does, and nutritionists consider this a healthy characteristic of these root vegetables.

*Quick Fix: Cut up an extra batch of potatoes, and freeze for a ready-to-bake option next time.

Charley's® Grilled Subs Menu Makeover

	Charley's® Lunch Chicken Buffalo Wrap, Cheddar Cheese Fries, Pepsi® (8 oz)	Charley's® Better Choice Philly Chicken Wrap, Kid's Fries, Diet Pepsi® (8 oz)	Menu Makeover Philly Chicken "Wrap and Roll," Cheesy Cheese "Un-fried" Fries, Diet Pepsi® (8 oz)
Calories	1764	866	495
Total Fat	119.5g	51.5g	10.2g
Sat. Fat	20g (2.5g trans)	11.5g (3g trans)	4.4g (0g trans)
Fiber	5g	6g	12.7g
Sugar	86g	5g	6.3g
Protein	60g	49g	44.7g

Philly Chicken "Wrap and Roll"

	Charley's® Chicken Buffalo Wrap	Charley's® Philly Chicken Wrap	Philly Chicken "Wrap and Roll"
Calories	610	500	296
Total Fat	35.5g	24.5g	6.9g
Sat. Fat	9.5g	7.5g	2.9g
Fiber	3g	3g	8.7g
Sugar	5g	5g	1.2g
Protein	46g	46g	35.1g

Philly Chicken "Wrap and Roll"

Ingredients:

- Nonstick cooking spray
- 3 ounces sliced or diced chicken breast
- 1 tablespoon chopped onion
- 1 tablespoon chopped red bell peppers
- ½ cup sliced mushrooms
- 1 (6-inch) Mission® Carb Balance whole wheat tortilla
- 1 slice Sargento® reduced fat provolone cheese
- ¼ cup shredded lettuce
- ¼ cup diced tomato
- 1 tablespoon honey mustard

Directions:

1: Spray skillet with nonstick spray, and put on medium heat.
2: Cook chicken until about 75% done, then add onion, peppers, and mushrooms. Stir in pan frequently until chicken is fully cooked.
3: Spoon mixture onto tortilla on a microwave safe plate.
4: Tear cheese in half, and lay on top of chicken.
5: Top with lettuce, tomato and honey mustard.
6: Wrap it up.
7: Slice in half, and serve.

Makes 1 serving.

*Lighten Up: Substitute provolone cheese with fat free cheese.

*Switch It Up: Substitute chicken with lean beef, turkey or ham.

*Nutrition Boost: Add shredded carrots, spinach, or onions.

*Quick Fix: Skip stove top cooking, and microwave pre-cooked meat.

Cheesy Cheese "Un-fried" Fries

	Charley's® Cheddar Cheese Fries	Cheesy Cheese "Un-fried" Fries (4.9 oz fries / 2 oz cheese sauce)
Calories	1054	258
Total Fat	84g	6.3g
Sat. Fat	15.5g	1.5g
Fiber	2g	3g
Sugar	0g	1.6g
Protein	14g	14.5g

Cheesy Cheese "Un-fried" Fries

Ingredients:

- For fries, follow recipe for "Un-fried" Fries on page 43.

- For Cheese Sauce, use ingredients below:
- 2 ounces 2% Velveeta® cheese
- 1 ounce fat free milk

Directions:

1: Mix ingredients in microwave-safe bowl.
2: Cook in microwave for 30 seconds.
3: Stir, and cook for an additional 30 seconds.

Makes 1 serving.

*Lighten Up: Make a thinner cheese sauce by using 2 ounces of fat free milk with 1 ounce of 2% Velveeta cheese.

*Switch It Up: Mix in 2 ounces of salsa to make it Mexican style.

*Nutrition Boost: Mix in 1 ounce of cauliflower. Cauliflower is low in calories and high in dietary fiber, folate, water and vitamin C. Cauliflower is similar to broccoli and cabbage by containing several phytochemicals, including sulforaphane, an anti-cancer compound. Cauliflower also contains substances which may improve the liver's ability to detoxify carcinogenic substances.

*Quick Fix: Heat up 1 ounce of Prego® three cheese sauce.

Burger King® Menu Makeover

	Burger King® Lunch Whopper® with Cheese, Medium Onion Rings, Medium Sprite	Burger King® Better Choice Veggie Bean Burger with Cheese, Garden Salad with Fat-free Ranch, Large Diet Coke®	Menu Makeover Blasted Bean Burger with Cheese, My-O-My Onion Rings, Sprite Zero® (24 oz)
Calories	1460	660	407
Total Fat	68g	26g	10.1g
Sat. Fat	18g	7.5g	3.5g
Fiber	3g	10g	10.6g
Sugar	96g	17g	7.3g
Protein	37g	31g	23.5g

Blasted Bean Burger

	Burger King® Whopper with Cheese	Blasted Bean Burger with Cheese
Calories	720	268
Total Fat	44g	7.5g
Sat. Fat	14g	3.5g
Fiber	2g	9.4g
Sugar	11g	5.2g
Protein	31g	19.4g

* TVP is a soy product you can substitute for ground meat in recipes. It's a less expensive, lower calorie, fat free alternative to ground beef.

Blasted Bean Burger

Ingredients:

- ½ cup quick-cooking oats
- 1 cup TVP (Textured Vegetable Protein)* See note on page 48.
- 1 teaspoon salt
- ½ cup cooked brown rice or quinoa
- 2 egg whites or ½ cup egg white substitute
- ½ cup chopped bell pepper
- ½ cup chopped onion
- 1 tablespoon minced garlic or 2-3 garlic cloves, pressed
- 1 (6-ounce) can tomato paste
- 1 (15-ounce) can black beans, rinsed and drained
- 1 tablespoon 2% shredded cheddar cheese, per burger
- 1 Arnold Select® Sandwich Thins 100% whole wheat bun, per burger

Directions:

1: Combine first nine ingredients into a food processor, and pulse until blended. Then add beans, and pulse until coarsely blended.
2: Spray large skillet with cooking spray, and preheat to medium.
3: Spray a ¼-cup measuring cup with cooking spray, scoop up mixture, and place in frying pan. Tap tops of burgers with spatula to flatten out.
4: Spray tops of burgers with cooking spray, and flip burger gently with a spatula when browned, after about 3 to 5 minutes.
5: Use spatula to further flatten burgers to desired size.
6: Continue to cook until both sides are browned! Top with cheese, and place on bun.

Makes 13 burgers.

*Lighten Up: Substitute 2% cheese with fat free cheese. Top with lettuce and tomato.

*Switch It Up: For a spicy alternative, add chili powder, Tabasco sauce, cayenne pepper, Worcestershire sauce, or horseradish. Add additional toppings by adding tomato, onion, pickle, ketchup, mustard, fat free salsa, sautéed mushrooms or reduced fat mayonnaise.

*Nutrition Boost: Use spinach leaves in place of lettuce.

*Quick Fix: Microwave a pre-made frozen vegetable burger.

My-O-My Onion Rings

Ingredients:

- 3 large onions
- ½ cup whole wheat flour
- 2 cups light Lay's® fat free potato chips or Baked Lay's®
- 2 cups panko bread crumbs
- ½ teaspoon each garlic powder, onion powder, dried thyme and oregano
- ¼ teaspoon cayenne pepper
- 2 egg whites
- 1 cup buttermilk
- Nonfat canola spray

Directions:

1: Preheat oven to 450°. Cut the onions into ½-inch thick slices, and separate into rings.
2: Place rings into a large resealable bag with ½ cup whole wheat flour. Close the bag and shake well, so all the onions are coated with flour. Set aside.
3: Place the potato chips in a food processor, and blend until they are finely ground. Then mix together panko crumbs and crushed chips in a shallow bowl, and add the seasonings. Mix well.
4: In a mixing bowl, beat egg whites until soft peaks or mounds form, but so tips of the peaks still droop over.
5: Pour buttermilk Into a large, deep bowl. Gently fold in the beaten egg whites; the batter should be light and fluffy.
6: Coat two 9" x 13" baking pans with nonfat canola spray. Hook an onion ring on your finger and dip it into the liquid batter, gently shaking off any excess, then dip it into the crumb/seasoning mixture. The rings won't be fully coated, but don't worry, they will still have a big crunch from the panko crumbs.
7: Place the rings in the prepared baking pans, and let sit in the fridge for 15 minutes.
8: After resting in fridge, place onion rings in the center of the oven for 18 to 20 minutes, or until they are golden brown.

Makes 8 servings.

*Lighten Up: For a surprisingly sweet, tasty, and only 20 calorie side dish, try this recipe: Take a large onion, cut off ends, and remove outer peel. Cut a deep "X" on the top of the onion. Crush one garlic clove and stick into onion. Sprinkle tops with beef bouillon granules and Parmesan cheese. Wrap onion in foil so it resembles a giant "Hershey's® Kiss!" Grill onion over medium high, for an hour, until tender. Serves 4.

*Switch It Up: Dip onion rings in this "Tasty Dip with a Twist." Mix 6 ounces Greek yogurt (has a thicker consistency than regular yogurt), 2 tablespoons light mayonnaise, 2 tablespoons honey, 2 tablespoons lime juice, 1 tablespoon parsley and 1 teaspoon horseradish. Chill for 30 minutes.

*Nutrition Boost: Increase the fiber in this recipe by replacing the potato chips with crushed All Bran® cereal or Fiber One®.

*Quick Fix: For a shorter version, just mix together 2 cups panko bread crumbs with 2 cups seasoned bread crumbs; then mix ½ cup Greek yogurt with ½ cup buttermilk. Follow steps 1 and 2 on facing page, then dip onion rings in yogurt/buttermilk mix, then bread crumb mixture. Bake as directed.

My-O-My Onion Rings

	Burger King® Medium Onion Rings	My-O-My Onion Rings
Calories	450	139
Total Fat	24g	2.6g
Sat. Fat	4g	0g
Fiber	1g	1.2g
Sugar	6g	2.1g
Protein	6g	4.1g

Arby's® Menu Makeover

	Arby's® Lunch Arby's® Pecan Chicken Salad Sandwich, Medium Curly Fries, Jamocha Shake	Arby's® Better Choice Ham and Swiss Cheese Melt, Applesauce, 1% Chocolate Milk	Menu Makeover Perfect Pick Pecan Chicken Salad, Sassy Seasoned Fries, Moooocha Mocha Shake
Calories	2030	550	528
Total Fat	90g	11g	14.1g
Sat. Fat	21g	4.5g	3g
Fiber	13g	4g	15.4g
Sugar	120g	50g	28.2g
Protein	56g	26g	22.6g

Perfect Pick Pecan Chicken Salad

	Arby's® Pecan Chicken Salad Sandwich with Wheat Bread and Lettuce	Perfect Pick Pecan Chicken Salad Two Slices Wheat Bread with Lettuce (35 calories each)
Calories	870	262
Total Fat	44g	11.9g
Sat. Fat	6g	1.7g
Fiber	7g	7.5g
Sugar	22g	6.6g
Protein	34g	14.2g

Perfect Pick Pecan Chicken Salad

Ingredients:

- 2 cups cooked chicken breast, cubed or shredded
- 2 cups Red Delicious apples, cored and chopped
- 1 cup sliced celery
- ¼ cup chopped onion
- ½ cup green grapes
- ¼ cup chopped toasted pecans and walnuts
- ½ cup Hellmann's® canola oil mayonnaise
- ½ cup Greek yogurt such as Oikos® (you may substitute plain light yogurt, if unavailable)
- 3-4 teaspoons lemon juice
- 2 teaspoons Dijon-style mustard
- ½ teaspoon garlic powder
- ¼ - ½ teaspoon poultry seasoning
- 1 teaspoon paprika
- 2 slices 35-calorie wheat bread

Directions:

1: Combine chicken, apples, celery, onion, grapes and nuts in bowl.
2: Blend mayonnaise, yogurt, lemon juice, mustard and seasonings; stir into chicken mixture.
3: Serve chicken salad on two slices of 35-calorie wheat bread.
4: Sprinkle with additional chopped pecans, if desired.

Makes 6 servings.

*Lighten Up: Use fat free mayonnaise. You can also spoon the chicken salad onto lettuce-lined plates, instead of serving on bread.

*Switch It Up: Replace 1 cup apples with 1 cup chopped pineapple. Quarter a cantaloupe to serve. Top quartered cantaloupe slices with ½ cup chicken salad.

*Nutrition Boost: Give your chicken salad a boost by adding 2 tablespoons flax seed! Just 2 tablespoons of ground flax seed contain more than 140% of the daily value for inflammation-reducing omega-3 fatty acids, and more lignans, a cancer-fighting plant chemical, than any other plant food.

*Quick Fix: Use canned or frozen pre-chopped chicken and pre-chopped vegetables from the deli section of the grocery store.

Sassy Seasoned Fries

	Arby's® Medium Curly Fries	Sassy Seasoned Fries
Calories	540	128
Total Fat	29g	0.2g
Sat. Fat	4g	0g
Fiber	6g	2.6g
Sugar	0g	1.6g
Protein	7g	3.5g

Sassy Seasoned Fries

Ingredients:

- 1 medium potato
- Olive oil cooking spray
- 1 teaspoon seasoning salt
- Salt, to taste (optional)

Directions:

1: Wash potato well, and slice into thin long sticks, including the skin.
2: Preheat oven to 450°.
3: Spray baking sheet.
4: If you can find a curly fry cutter, use that; otherwise, just slice potato as desired.
5: Spread potato slices on baking sheet, and spray potatoes with olive oil cooking spray.
6: Bake for about 15 to 20 minutes or until golden brown.
7: Flip potato slices over with a spatula, and continue baking for an additional 10 to 15 minutes, until golden brown.

Makes 1 serving.

*Lighten Up: Use butternut squash in place of regular potatoes.

*Switch It Up: For an alternative flavor, season with ranch powder, cheese powder, or barbecue powder.

*Nutrition Boost: Use sweet potatoes in place of regular potatoes.

*Quick Fix: Cut up an extra batch of potatoes, and freeze for ready-to-bake option next time.

Moooocha Mocha Shake

	Arby's® Jamocha Shake (12 oz)	Moooocha Mocha Shake (12 oz)
Calories	610	138
Total Fat	17g	2g
Sat. Fat	11g	1.3g
Fiber	1g	5.3g
Sugar	97g	20g
Protein	15g	4.9g

Moooocha Mocha Shake

Ingredients:

- 1 cup cold, strong coffee
- ½ cup skim milk, light soy milk, or unsweetened almond milk
- 3 packets Splenda®
- 2 cups fat free chocolate ice cream or frozen yogurt
- ½ teaspoon vanilla extract
- 1 cup crushed ice

Directions:

1: Place coffee, milk and Splenda® in blender, and blend until mixed.
2: Mix in ice cream, vanilla and ice. Blend until smooth.

Makes 3 (12-ounce) servings.

*Lighten Up: Replace 1 cup frozen yogurt with 2 tablespoons chilled chocolate pudding and 4 ice cubes or more, until desired consistency.

*Switch It Up: Throw in a small handful of Teddy Grahams®, a 100-calorie Oreo® Thin Crisps pack, or a handful of chocolate dried cereal such as Coco Puffs®.

*Nutrition Boost: Increase the fiber by blending in one frozen or chilled banana.

*Quick Fix: Mix together 2 cups fat free or low fat coffee ice cream, 1 cup skim milk, 1 teaspoon vanilla, and 1 tablespoon reduced sugar chocolate syrup.

Subway® Menu Makeover

	Subway® Lunch 6" Tuna Sub on Italian Herb and Cheese Bread, Sun Chips®, Oatmeal Cookie, Reduced Fat Chocolate Milk (12 oz)	Subway® Better Choice 6" Turkey Sandwich with American Cheese, Lay's® Light Chips, Apple Slices, Yogurt, Minute Maid® Light (12 oz)	Menu Makeover Tropical Tuna Salad on 6" Spectacular Seasoned Sub, Classic Chips, Original Oatmeal Supreme Cookies, Skim Milk (8 oz)
Calories	1240	530	737
Total Fat	54.5g	5g	11.8g
Sat. Fat	16g	1g	2.3g
Fiber	7g	9g	19.8g
Sugar	67g	26g	21.7g
Protein	41g	25g	52.5g

Tropical Tuna Salad

	Subway® Tuna (without bread)	Tropical Tuna Salad
Calories	280	185
Total Fat	24.5g	5.6g
Sat. Fat	3.5g	0.8g
Fiber	1g	4.4g
Sugar	2g	16.6g
Protein	11g	23.4g

Tropical Tuna Salad

Ingredients:
- 4 grapes
- 1 tablespoon pineapple tidbits in light syrup
- 1 (12-ounce) can tuna in water
- 2 tablespoons light mayonnaise
- 2 tablespoons fat free apricot mango yogurt
- 1 tablespoon chopped celery

Directions:
1: Dice grapes and pineapple into smaller pieces.
2: Drain tuna, and combine with mayonnaise, yogurt, celery, and fruit.
3: Mix well. Serve tuna salad on Spectacular Seasoned Subs. See recipe on page 60.

Makes 2 servings.

*Lighten Up: Serve tuna salad on a bed of fresh lettuce or inside a hollowed out green pepper or tomato, instead of using bread.

*Switch It Up: Try a variety of different fruits such as cranberries, or try some extra vegetables such as diced jicama or avocado. You can also add some extra protein by chopping up a hardboiled egg into the mix.

*Nutrition Boost: Beans are surprisingly high in protein and rich in iron, which is important for your cells and helps deliver oxygen to your lungs. Add 1 (19-ounce) can of drained chickpeas to the mix! You can mash the beans into a smooth paste by using a blender or food processor, or use the beans whole for a different texture.

*Quick Fix: Prepare salad the night before for an easy and healthy snack when your tummy starts to rumble.

Spectacular Seasoned Subs

Ingredients:

- 1 cup plus 1 tablespoon warm water, divided
- 1 teaspoon sugar
- 1 tablespoon dry yeast
- 1 teaspoon salt
- 1 teaspoon butter
- 2 cups bread flour
- ½ teaspoon dough enhancer
- 1 tablespoon Italian seasoning
- 1 cup fat free cheddar cheese

Directions:

1: Prepare yeast by pouring 1 cup warm water (about the temperature of bath water), sugar, and yeast into a bowl. Let sit for 10 minutes, until a tan bubbly foam develops.
2: Mix in remaining ingredients, except 1 tablespoon warm water and cheese, until well blended.
3: Cover bowl with a towel, and let rise for 30 minutes in a warm place.
4: Punch down dough, and let rise for another 30 minutes.
5: Shape dough into 3 (12"-long) tubes.
6: Place dough tubes on a cookie sheet, into unheated oven, with cake pan of hot water on shelf below.
7: Spray or brush tops of dough with 1 tablespoon warm water at beginning of proofing. Wait for 15 minutes, and turn oven on to 300° for 20 seconds, then off. Wait another 15 minutes, and repeat the above oven directions. Wait for 30 minutes, and repeat the oven directions a third time. Allow dough to rise for another 30 minutes.
8: Then turn oven on and bake at 325° for 20 minutes.
9: Top bread with cheese, and turn heat to 350°. Bake for an additional 20 minutes.
10: Remove from oven, and place on rack for cooling.

Makes six (6-inch) subs.

*Lighten Up: Save a few calories by skipping the shredded cheddar cheese.

*Switch It Up: Mix ⅓ cup chopped dates and ⅓ cup nuts into the dough.

*Nutrition Boost: Top subs with ½ cup whole flax seeds before baking. Flax seeds may help reduce inflammation, blood pressure and colon cancer risk from its high omega-3 content.

*Quick Fix: Use a low calorie sub bun, instead of baking bread, or freeze bread dough after step 4, and bake at a later time.

Spectacular Seasoned Subs

	Subway® Italian Herb and Cheese (one 6-inch sub)	Spectacular Seasoned Subs (one 6-inch sub)
Calories	250	206
Total Fat	5g	1.4g
Sat. Fat	2g	0.5g
Fiber	2g	1.1g
Sugar	5g	0.7g
Protein	10g	10.8g

Add Classic Chips to complete this meal. See recipe on page 141.

Classic Chips

	Sun Chips (1.5 oz bag)	Classic Chips (1.5 oz or 12 chips)
Calories	210	120
Total Fat	9g	3g
Sat. Fat	1.5g	1.5g
Fiber	3g	10.5g
Sugar	3g	1.5g
Protein	4g	4.5g

Original Oatmeal Supreme Cookies

Ingredients:

- ½ cup Rice Krispies® cereal, crushed
- 1 cup Kashi® GOLEAN Crunch!®, crushed
- ¼ cup Fiber One® cereal, crushed
- 1 ½ cups Quaker® old-fashioned oats
- 1 cup unbleached all-purpose flour
- 3 tablespoons brown sugar
- 1 tablespoon cinnamon
- ½ teaspoon baking powder
- ½ teaspoon baking soda
- 3 tablespoons apple butter
- 1 tablespoon vanilla extract
- 2 egg whites, beaten
- ½ cup acorn squash, cooked and puréed
- ½ cup unsweetened applesauce
- 2 tablespoons Walden Farms® calorie free pancake syrup
- ⅓ cup raisins
- Butter-flavored PAM® spray

Directions:

1: Preheat oven to 350°.
2: In a resealable plastic bag, crush cereals. Combine all dry ingredients in a large mixing bowl.
3: In a second bowl, combine apple butter, vanilla, beaten egg whites, puréed squash, applesauce and syrup.
4: Slowly add dry mix into wet ingredients, while stirring.
5: Add in raisins or chips and peanut butter, if using the "Switch It Up" option.
6: Spray cookie sheet with butter-flavored PAM®, and place one rounded tablespoon of dough onto sheet, spaced at least an inch apart. Use the back of a fork to press cookies flat.
7: Bake for 15 to 20 minutes, then place onto cooling rack for 5 minutes.

Makes 24 cookies.

*Lighten Up: While our cookie recipe is lower in calories and fat than a standard cookie, you can get more vitamins and minerals by snacking on one whole cup fresh berries with fat free whipped cream for roughly the same amount of calories.

*Switch It Up: Add ½ cup mini chocolate chips and ¼ cup peanut butter to the batter for a chocolate peanut butter cookie.

*Nutrition Boost: Add ½ cup fresh blueberries in place of the raisins. Raisins are high in fiber, but also high in calories from sugar. One cup of blueberries only contains 80 calories, whereas ¼ cup of raisins contains 120 calories. Blueberries also contain more health benefits.

*Quick Fix: Replace acorn squash with ½ cup pumpkin or 1 whole banana, or add an additional cup of apple butter, and leave out the acorn squash and applesauce. To reduce the amount of ingredients, use 1 ¾ cups Kashi® GOLEAN Crunch!® cereal in place of both the Fiber One® and Rice Krispies®.

Original Oatmeal Supreme Cookies

	Subway® Oatmeal Raisin Cookies 1 cookie (1.58 oz)	Original Oatmeal Supreme Cookies 1 cookie (1.7 oz)
Calories	200	96
Total Fat	8g	0.8g
Sat. Fat	4g	0g
Fiber	1g	2.2g
Sugar	17g	6.6g
Protein	3g	2.8g

Dairy Queen® Menu Makeover

	Dairy Queen® Lunch Fish Fillet Sandwich with Cheese, Fries, Medium Chocolate Malt	Dairy Queen® Better Choice Grilled Chicken Wrap, Small Fries, Diet Pepsi® or Water, DQ® Fudge Bar (no sugar added)	Menu Makeover Fresh-R-Fish Sandwich, "Un-fried" Fries, Chocolishus Chocolate Malt
Calories	1690	440	793
Total Fat	57g	21g	12.3g
Sat. Fat	21g	4.5g	4g
Fiber	5g	9g	11g
Sugar	137g	5g	25.9g
Protein	42g	18g	49.4g

Fresh-R-Fish Sandwich

	DQ® Fish Fillet Sandwich with Cheese	Fresh-R-Fish Sandwich (including sauce)
Calories	480	320
Total Fat	22g	6.2g
Sat. Fat	5g	0.7g
Fiber	2g	9.7g
Sugar	7g	9.3g
Protein	18g	30.5g

Fresh-R-Fish Sandwich

Ingredients:

- 4 Gorton's® frozen grilled lemon butter fish fillets
- 1 cup Fiber One® original bran cereal
- ½ teaspoon garlic powder
- ¼ teaspoon salt
- ¼ teaspoon pepper

- ½ cup skim milk
- Canola oil spray
- 4 whole wheat buns
- 4 slices fat free American cheese
- 4 lettuce leaves

Directions:

1: Defrost fish.
2: Heat oven to 350°.
3: Place cereal in a resealable food storage bag, and seal tightly.
4: Finely crush cereal with a rolling pin or meat mallet (or crush in a food processor).
5: In shallow bowl, mix cereal, garlic powder, salt and pepper. In another shallow bowl, place milk. Dip fish pieces into milk; then coat with cereal mixture.
6: Spray baking sheet with canola oil, and place coated fish fillets on sheet to bake for 10 minutes. After 10 minutes, flip carefully with spatula, and bake for another 5 minutes, until fish flakes easily with fork.
7: Slice buns and place 1 cooked fish on bottom bun. Top with cheese slice, lettuce and top of bun.

Makes 4 servings.

*Lighten Up: Replace regular bun with a 100 calorie bun.

*Switch It Up: Add 1 tablespoon chili powder to seasoning to make a spicy sandwich.

*Nutrition Boost: Add sliced tomatoes to sandwich. Tomatoes are high in the antioxidant vitamins beta-carotene, vitamin C and vitamin E, as well as the carotenoid lycopene. This means that tomatoes are helpful in preventing heart disease and cancers. Tomatoes are also high in potassium, but very low in sodium, which means they help combat high blood pressure and fluid retention.

*Quick Fix: Replace Fiber One® cereal and seasoning with 1 cup seasoned bread crumbs.

Chocolishus Chocolate Malt

Ingredients:

- ½ cup Edy's® Slow Churned® vanilla ice cream
- ½ cup Cool Whip Free® topping
- 3 tablespoons Carnation® malted milk powder
- 1 cup skim milk or light soy milk
- 1 cup crushed ice
- 1 packet Swiss Miss® diet cocoa mix

Directions:

1: Place all ingredients in blender, and blend on high until smooth.

Optional: Top with 2 tablespoons Cool Whip Free®, 1 ounce mini chocolate chips and a maraschino cherry for an additional 70 calories.

Makes 1 serving.

*Lighten Up: Substitute one packet of Cool Splashers® sugar free chocolate malt mix for Carnation® malted milk.

*Switch It Up: Add a small banana.

*Nutrition Boost: Add a scoop of protein powder. Protein can help keep your energy up, and keep you feeling fuller longer.

*Quick Fix: Freeze an extra batch for future use.

Chocolishus Chocolate Malt

	DQ® Medium Chocolate Malt (20 oz)	Chocolishus Chocolate Malt (approx. 20 oz)
Calories	900	345
Total Fat	22g	5.9g
Sat. Fat	14g	3.3g
Fiber	0g	1g
Sugar	130g	15g
Protein	20g	15.4g

Add "Un-fried" Fries to complete this meal. See recipe on page 43.

"Un-fried" Fries

	DQ® Medium Fries (4.1 oz)	"Un-fried" Fries (4.9 oz)
Calories	310	128
Total Fat	13g	0.2g
Sat. Fat	2g	0g
Fiber	3g	3g
Sugar	0g	1.6g
Protein	4g	3.5g

Dairy Queen® Menu Makeover

	Dairy Queen® Lunch Footlong Beef Hot Dog, Chili Cheese Fries, Medium Mt. Dew®, Small Oreo® Cookies Blizzard®	Dairy Queen® Better Choice Beef Hot Dog, Side Salad with Fat Free Ranch, Diet Pepsi®, Small Hot Fudge Sundae	Menu Makeover Fantastic Fat Free Franks (2 franks), Chillin' Chili Cheese Fries, Coolest Cookie 'n Cream Shake, Diet Mt. Dew®
Calories	2370	650	899
Total Fat	106g	27g	20.9g
Sat. Fat	39g	14g	11.5g
Fiber	12g	3g	21.2g
Sugar	135g	48g	45.5g
Protein	57g	19g	32.4g

Fantastic Fat Free Franks

	DQ® Footlong Beef Hot Dog with Bun, Ketchup and Mustard	Fantastic Fat Free Franks (2 franks) with Ketchup, Mustard and 1 Wonder® Light Bun
Calories	560	169
Total Fat	35g	12g
Sat. Fat	14g	7g
Fiber	2g	4.2g
Sugar	6g	3.5g
Protein	20g	14g

Fantastic Fat Free Franks

Ingredients:
- 2 fat free Ball Park® hot dogs
- 1 Wonder® light hot dog bun

Directions:
1: Heat up hot dogs as directed.
2: Cut bun in half, and place 1 hot dog in each half bun.
3: Top with ketchup and mustard.

Makes 1 serving.

*Lighten Up: Have just one hot dog.

*Switch It Up: Top with relish or chili sauce, or replace bun with a spinach or wheat wrap.

*Nutrition Boost: Top with sauerkraut; it's an excellent source of vitamin C, lactobacilli and other nutrients. Replace bun with a whole wheat bun. Or replace fat free hot dog with a soy hot dog found in the organic section of your grocery store.

*Quick Fix: This is about as quick as it gets!

Chillin' Chili Cheese Fries

	DQ® Chili Cheese Fries	Chillin' Chili Cheese Fries (½ cup chili and ¼ cup cheese)
Calories	1240	394
Total Fat	71g	0.2g
Sat. Fat	28g	0g
Fiber	9g	14.5g
Sugar	4g	13.3g
Protein	34g	7g

Chillin' Chili Cheese Fries

Ingredients:

- For fries, follow recipe for "Un-fried" Fries. See recipe on page 43. (* Note: Fry recipe makes 1 serving. Increase as needed.)

- For chili sauce and cheese, use ingredients below:
- 1 (12-ounce) bottle Heinz® chili sauce
- ½ cup Textured Vegetable Protein*
- 1 package Lawry's® chili seasoning mix
- ¾ cup water
- 1 teaspoon Worcestershire sauce
- 1 tablespoon Dijon mustard
- ½ teaspoon onion powder
- 1 (14.5-ounce) can chili ready diced tomatoes
- 2 cups 2% shredded sharp cheddar cheese

Directions:

1: Combine all ingredients, except cheese, into a medium pot, and heat over medium high heat until it starts to boil. Stir frequently.
2: Reduce to low heat, and simmer for 10 minutes.
3: Spoon ½ cup mixture over fries, and top with ¼ cup cheese.

Makes 8 servings of chili sauce.

*Lighten Up: Use fat free cheese.

*Switch It Up: Add salsa into chili sauce for a Mexican flavor.

*Nutrition Boost: Add 1 cup cooked kidney beans. Beans are an excellent source of fiber, protein, folate and iron.

*Quick Fix: Use some leftover chili (just made or previously made and frozen) as the topping. Just add cheese.

* TVP is a soy product you can substitute for ground meat in recipes. It's a less expensive, lower calorie, fat free alternative to ground beef.

Coolest Cookie 'n Cream Shake

	DQ® Small Oreo® Cookies Blizzard® (10 oz)	Coolest Cookie 'n Cream Shake
Calories	550	336
Total Fat	20g	8.7g
Sat. Fat	10g	4.5g
Fiber	1g	2.5g
Sugar	61g	28.7g
Protein	12g	11.4g

Coolest Cookie 'n Cream Shake

Ingredients:

- ½ cup Edy's® Slow Churned® cookies 'n cream ice cream
- ½ cup Edy's® Slow Churned® no sugar added vanilla ice cream
- ½ cup skim milk
- 2 tablespoons Cool Whip Free® topping
- 4 single chocolate graham crackers

Directions:

1: Combine all ingredients into blender or food processor.
2: Blend carefully until mixed well, but not liquefied.
3: Pour into cup, and enjoy as an occasional special treat!

* Vary ingredients as needed to create your favorite flavors. For example, to make a cookie dough shake, substitute Slow Churned® Cookie Dough for Cookies 'n Cream and ¼ cup sugar free chocolate chips for the graham crackers.

Makes 8 (½-cup) servings.

*Lighten Up: Save 20 calories, and replace graham crackers with a 100-calorie Oreo® Thin Crisps pack.

*Switch It Up: Use Edy's® Slow Churned® chocolate ice cream in place of vanilla ice cream.

*Nutrition Boost: Add ½ of a banana to increase the fiber and potassium.

*Quick Fix: Freeze an extra batch for future use.

Steak 'n Shake® Menu Makeover

	Steak 'n Shake® Lunch Turkey Melt, Baked Beans, Regular Strawberry Milkshake	Steak 'n Shake® Better Choice Single Steak Burger, Apples and Grapes, Side Salad, Diet Coke®	Menu Makeover Totally Turkey Club Melt, Beanerific Baked Beans, Stupendous Strawberry Shake
Calories	1975	377	696
Total Fat	86g	11g	8.3g
Sat. Fat	29g	3.5g	2.9g
Fiber	13g	3.8g	6.8g
Sugar	156g	11.9g	45.6g
Protein	65g	17g	45.5g

Totally Turkey Club Melt

	Steak 'n Shake® Turkey Melt	Totally Turkey Club Melt
Calories	914	354
Total Fat	64g	8g
Sat. Fat	14.5g	2.8g
Fiber	0g	2.6g
Sugar	15g	15.7g
Protein	34g	30.1g

Totally Turkey Club Melt

Ingredients:
- 2 slices Jennie-O® extra lean turkey bacon
- Nonstick cooking spray
- 2 slices whole wheat bread
- I Can't Believe It's Not Butter® pump spray
- 3 ounces sliced, cooked turkey breast
- 1 slice Sargento® reduced fat provolone cheese
- 1 tablespoon honey mustard

Directions:
1: Pre-cook turkey bacon as directed.
2: Spray fry pan with nonstick cooking spray.
3: Heat skillet on medium high heat.
4: Spray tops of bread with butter spray.
5: Place turkey bacon, turkey breast, cheese and honey mustard between bread, and place in skillet.
6: Turn sandwich with spatula until both sides are golden and cheese is melted.

Makes 1 sandwich.

*Lighten Up: Hold the turkey bacon.

*Switch It Up: Use cooked ham or chicken in place of turkey breast.

*Nutrition Boost: Add fresh spinach leaves, tomato and pickles.

*Quick Fix: Toast bread instead of grilling; assemble, and serve!

Beanerific Baked Beans

	Steak 'n Shake® Baked Beans	Beanerific Baked Beans (½ cup)
Calories	352	152
Total Fat	0g	0g
Sat. Fat	0g	0g
Fiber	12g	6g
Sugar	32g	5.6g
Protein	14g	6g

Beanerific Baked Beans

Ingredients:
- 1 (16-ounce) can Bush's® Best seasoned pinto beans
- 1 tablespoon Kraft® Thick 'n Spicy brown sugar barbecue sauce
- 1 teaspoon yellow mustard
- 1 tablespoon dark brown sugar
- ¼ cup ketchup

Directions:
1: Mix all ingredients in a pot.
2: Cook over low-medium heat for 5 minutes, stirring occasionally, until heated.

Makes 4 servings.

*Lighten Up: Use Heinz® low sugar ketchup.

*Switch It Up: Add 1 tablespoon hot sauce.

*Nutrition Boost: Mix in diced onions and chopped peppers.

*Quick Fix: Combine all ingredients in a microwave safe bowl, and cook until thoroughly heated.

Stupendous Strawberry Shake

	Steak 'n Shake® Regular Strawberry Milkshake (22 oz)	Stupendous Strawberry Shake (approx. 20 oz)
Calories	709	180
Total Fat	22g	0.3g
Sat. Fat	14.5g	0.1g
Fiber	1g	0.9g
Sugar	109g	21.3g
Protein	17g	11.4g

Stupendous Strawberry Shake

Ingredients:
- 4 frozen, unsweetened strawberries
- 4 ounces skim milk or light soy milk
- 6 ounces fat free vanilla yogurt
- ½ teaspoon vanilla extract
- 2 teaspoons sugar

Directions:
1: Place all ingredients in blender, and blend on high until smooth.

* If using fresh strawberries, add ice for a more frozen consistency.

Makes 1 serving.

*Lighten up: Substitute 1 packet Splenda® for sugar.

*Switch it up: Substitute frozen strawberries with any other kind of frozen or fresh fruit.

*Nutrition Boost: Sneak in some greens by adding ¼ cup broccoli tops to the shake before blending.

*Quick fix: Grab a Dannon® Light & Fit® drinkable yogurt smoothie.

Chipotle® Menu Makeover

	Chipotle® Lunch Chicken Burrito, Chips & Guac, Pepsi® (24 oz)	Chipotle® Better Choice Healthy Burrito Bowl (Chicken, Vegetables, Beans, Salsa & Cheese), Cilantro-Lime Rice, Diet Pepsi® (24 oz)	Menu Makeover Buff Burrito, Go Green Guacamole & Classic Chips, Diet Pepsi® (24 oz)
Calories	2155	609	727
Total Fat	91g	16g	22.6g
Sat. Fat	26g	0.5g	6g
Fiber	34g	13g	25.4g
Sugar	100g	11.5g	9.1g
Protein	72g	42g	40.1g

Buff Burrito

	Chipotle® Chicken Burrito (with black beans, rice, chicken, salsa, sour cream, cheese, and guacamole)	Buff Burrito
Calories	1135	502
Total Fat	51g	12.3g
Sat. Fat	20g	4.6g
Fiber	20g	19.6g
Sugar	11g	5.3g
Protein	62g	33.5g

Buff Burrito

Ingredients:

- Canola oil spray
- 8 ounces diced chicken breast
- 1 cup water
- 1 cup canned black beans
- 1 cup cooked brown rice
- 1 package burrito seasoning
- 4 ounces 2% Kraft® shredded Mexican four cheese mixture
- 4 Mission® Carb Balance whole wheat tortillas
- 8 tablespoons fat free sour cream
- 2 cups diced tomatoes

Directions:

1: Spray frying pan with canola spray.
2: Cook chicken on medium heat, until no pink is left inside.
3: Add water, beans, cooked rice and seasoning into pan.
4: Simmer and stir until mixed well, and water is mostly absorbed.
5: Spread cheese over tortilla, and heat in microwave for 20 seconds.
6: Put chicken mixture on one side of tortilla; top with sour cream and tomatoes.
7: Tuck edges in, and roll.

Makes 4 burritos.

*Lighten Up: Use fat free cheese, and replace chicken with extra beans.

*Switch It Up: Replace chicken with beef.

*Nutrition Boost: Add ½ cup diced bell pepper and onions. Even though onions get a bad name for giving us unpleasant breath, they contain a surprising number of health benefits for inhibiting the cells in our body called osteoclasts, which break down bone. Onions are also anti-inflammatory, heart healthy, they reduce blood sugar, and may lower cancer risk.

*Quick Fix: Purchase Amy's® bean and cheese frozen burritos in the organic section of the grocery store, and microwave for 2 minutes until done.

Go Green Guacamole & Classic Chips

	Chipotle® Chips & Guac	Go Green Guacamole & Classic Chips (½ cup and 8 chips)
Calories	720	225
Total Fat	40g	10.3g
Sat. Fat	6g	1.4g
Fiber	14g	5.8g
Sugar	5g	3.8g
Protein	10g	6.6g

Go Green Guacamole

Ingredients:

- 1 cup frozen peas
- 1 small ripe avocado, peeled, pit removed
- ⅔ cup fat free sour cream
- ½ cup cilantro, stems removed
- 1 small ripe tomato, chopped
- ½ cup onion
- 1 teaspoon fresh lime juice

Directions:

1: Defrost peas in the microwave or in the refrigerator.
2: Mix all ingredients in the food processor, and pulse a few times until blended to desired consistency.
3: Serve with our Classic Chips. See recipe on page 141.

Makes 6 servings (½ cup serving of guacamole and 8 chips).

*Lighten Up: Decrease portion size by dishing out only ¼ cup guacamole per serving.

*Switch It Up: Spice it up by chopping in 1 fresh jalapeno pepper.

*Nutrition Boost: Before blending, add ¼ cup salsa to increase the lycopenes - a heart healthy, cancer-fighting compound.

*Quick Fix: Use a packet mix of guacamole, and prepare as directed, using fat free ingredients.

Qdoba® Menu Makeover

	Qdoba® Lunch 3-Cheese Nachos, Bottle of Lipton® Lemon Brisk Sweetened Iced Tea (20 oz)	Qdoba® Better Choice Chicken Soft Taco with Lettuce, Salsa, Fajita Vegetables, Tortilla Soup, Large Diet Soda (20 oz)	Menu Makeover No Nonsense Bean and Cheese Nacho, Diet or Unsweetened Iced Tea
Calories	1295	360	509
Total Fat	59g	13.5g	9.4g
Sat. Fat	20g	3.5g	3g
Fiber	29g	3g	10.8g
Sugar	47g	2g	13.2g
Protein	26g	16g	24.3g

No Nonsense Bean and Cheese Nacho

	Qdoba® 3-Cheese Nachos (chips, 3-cheese queso, black beans, sour cream, guacamole and salsa)	No Nonsense Bean and Cheese Nacho
Calories	1145	509
Total Fat	59g	9.4g
Sat. Fat	20g	3g
Fiber	29g	10.8g
Sugar	7g	13.2g
Protein	26g	24.3g

No Nonsense Bean and Cheese Nacho

Ingredients:

- 2 (8-inch) Mission® whole wheat 96% fat free tortillas
- Canola oil spray
- 2 ounces (1 ½-inch slice) Velveeta® 2% cheese
- ¼ cup black beans or pinto beans
- ½ cup Del Monte® diced tomatoes with zesty mild green chiles
- 4 tablespoons salsa
- 1 teaspoon chili powder
- 3 tablespoons fat free sour cream

Directions:

1: Preheat oven to 400°.
2: Cut each tortilla into 8 triangles.
3: Spray baking sheet and both sides of tortillas; spread onto sheet.
4: Bake for 15 to 20 minutes, until desired crispness is obtained.
5: Place cheese, beans, tomatoes, salsa and chili powder in a microwave safe dish.
6: Microwave for 1 minute; stir. Continue heating and stirring in 30 second increments until cheese is melted.
7: Place chips on a plate, and pour melted cheese and bean mixture over them. Top with sour cream.

Makes 1 serving.

*Lighten Up: Leave out the sour cream.

*Switch It Up: Use corn tortillas instead of whole wheat.

*Nutrition Boost: Add diced bell pepper into cheese.

*Quick Fix: Use store-bought baked tortilla chips.

Taco Bell® Menu Makeover

	Taco Bell® Lunch Chipotle Steak Taco Salad, Caramel Apple Empanada, Tropical Fruit Punch (20 oz)	**Taco Bell® Better Choice** Fresco Steak Taco Salad without Shell, Cinnamon Twists, Water	**Menu Makeover** Top Taco Salad, Caramel Apple Empa-wow-as, Crystal Light® Fruit Punch (16 oz)
Calories	1475	390	608
Total Fat	72g	14g	15.3g
Sat. Fat	13.5g	2g	3.6g
Fiber	17g	7g	5.3g
Sugar	98g	13g	32.4g
Protein	33g	19g	45.4g

Top Taco Salad

	Taco Bell® Chipotle Steak Taco Salad	**Top Taco Salad**
Calories	900	434
Total Fat	57g	10.8g
Sat. Fat	11g	1.6g
Fiber	8g	4.3g
Sugar	7g	16.2g
Protein	28g	42.7g

Top Taco Salad

Ingredients:

- 4 (8-inch) Mission® Carb Balance flour tortillas
- 12 ounces Perdue® Fit & Easy ground turkey breast
- 1 packet Taco Bell® taco seasoning mix
- ½ cup water
- 8 tablespoons Taco Bell® Home Originals Thick and Chunky Salsa
- 1 cup canned pinto or black beans
- 4 cups shredded romaine lettuce
- 4 ounces 2% reduced fat sharp cheddar cheese
- 1 cup fresh diced tomatoes
- 8 tablespoons fat free sour cream
- 8 tablespoons light ranch dressing

Directions:

1: Preheat oven to 425°. Crumple 4 large sheets of foil to make four (3-inch) balls; place on baking sheet. Place 1 tortilla on top of each ball; spray tortilla with cooking spray. Bake 6 to 8 minutes, or until tortillas are golden brown. (Tortillas will drape over balls as they bake.)
2: Meanwhile, brown meat in large nonstick skillet on medium-high heat, stirring occasionally, until no longer pink. Drain off fat.
3: Stir in taco seasoning, water, salsa and beans. Cook uncovered, stirring occasionally, for about 5 minutes, until most of liquid is absorbed.
4: Place 1 tortilla shell on each of four serving plates. Fill evenly with salad greens, meat mixture, cheese and tomatoes. Top with sour cream and dressing.

Makes 4 servings.

*Lighten Up: Substitute fat free cheese for the 2%.

*Switch It Up: Replace ground turkey with 98% extra lean ground beef.

*Nutrition Boost: Add 1 cup finely chopped bell peppers when cooking meat for even more fiber and vitamins.

*Quick Fix: Substitute a serving of baked tortilla chips for tortilla shell, and use pre-packaged washed and cut lettuce.

Caramel Apple Empa-wow-as

	Taco Bell® Caramel Apple Empanada	Caramel Apple Empa-wow-as (1 empa-wow-a)
Calories	310	174
Total Fat	15g	4.5g
Sat. Fat	2.5g	2g
Fiber	2g	1g
Sugar	13g	16.2g
Protein	3g	2.7g

Caramel Apple Empa-wow-as

Ingredients:

- 1 package reduced fat crescent rolls
- 1 ½ cups apples, peeled and chopped
- 4 teaspoons cinnamon, divided
- 2 teaspoons lemon juice
- ½ cup fat free caramel dip
- 1 tablespoon sugar
- I Can't Believe It's Not Butter® pump spray

Directions:

1: Lightly grease 2 baking sheets.
2: Separate crescent rolls into 8 pieces. Flatten and stretch each piece.
3: Mix apple slices with 2 teaspoons of cinnamon and lemon juice.
4: Add mixture evenly to each roll.
5: Add 1 tablespoon caramel to each roll.
6: Fold dough over apples, and pinch to close openings.
7: Mix remaining 2 teaspoons cinnamon and 1 tablespoon sugar.
8: Spray each empa-wow-a with butter spray; sprinkle with cinnamon/sugar.
9: Place on prepared baking sheets, and bake empa-wow-as for 12 minutes or until golden brown. Serve warm.

Makes 8 servings.

*Lighten Up: To save calories, opt for an apple dipped in fat free caramel sauce instead.

*Switch It Up: Mix in other fruits like peaches and cherries.

*Nutrition Boost: Throw in some additional diced apple. Apples have a number of health benefits, and contain a high amount of vitamin C. As the saying goes: "An apple a day keeps the doctor away."

*Quick Fix: Use pita bread. Stuff with apple mix, and bake in oven.

Restaurant Lunch

Page 92
T.G.I. Friday's®
Menu Makeover Recipes

"Poppin'" Potato Skins,
Chicken
Cruncher Salad,
Berry-licious
Lemon Freeze

T.G.I. Friday's® Menu Makeover

	T.G.I. Friday's® Lunch	T.G.I. Friday's® Better Choice	Menu Makeover
	Pecan-Crusted Chicken Salad without Dressing, Loaded Potato Skins (½ order), Strawberry Lemonade Slush	Mediterranean Chicken Salad without Low-fat Cilantro Lime Dressing, Pot Stickers, Diet Coke®	"Poppin'" Potato Skins, Chicken Cruncher Salad, Berry-licious Lemon Freeze
Calories	1766	675	678
Calories w/ dressing	2356 w/ balsamic salad dressing	835 w/ cilantro dressing	723 w/ 2 tablespoons light balsamic dressing
Total Fat	109g *	14.5g	16.4g
Sat. Fat	28g *	0g	6.8g
Fiber	11g *	0g	13.7g
Sugar	78.5g *	0g	27.7g
Protein	88.3g *	36g	38.2g

* Nutrition facts for Strawberry Lemonade Slush were unavailable.

"Poppin'" Potato Skins

	T.G.I. Friday's® Loaded Potato Skins (½ of the appetizer served)	"Poppin'" Potato Skins (½ recipe)
Calories	675	240
Total Fat	47.9g	6.7g
Sat. Fat	21g	3.5g
Fiber	9g	4.6g
Sugar	4.6g	0.9g
Protein	24.3g	13.4g

"Poppin'" Potato Skins

Ingredients:
- 2 large russet potatoes
- 2 slices Jennie-O® turkey bacon (extra lean)
- Canola oil spray
- Kosher salt and pepper, to taste
- 2 ounces reduced fat 2% Kraft® sharp cheddar cheese
- 4 tablespoons fat free sour cream
- 4 tablespoons chopped fresh green onions

Directions:
1: Scrub the potatoes clean; then bake the potatoes using your favorite method (either oven or microwave).
2: While potatoes are cooking, prepare turkey bacon as directed, let cool, and then break into crumbles.
3: When the potatoes are done, let cool enough to handle safely. Cut lengthwise in half, and scoop out potato, leaving about ¼" of potato on skin.
4: Preheat oven to 450°.
5: Place skins on roasting pan, spray both sides of potato with canola oil spray, and sprinkle with salt.
6: Cook for 10 minutes; then flip and cook for another 10 minutes.
7: Remove from oven, and top inside of potatoes with cheese, bacon and pepper.
8: Broil for 2 minutes.
9: Place onto serving plate; top with sour cream and green onions.

Makes 2 servings.

*Lighten Up: Use fat free cheese.

*Switch It Up: Add a tablespoon of salsa to each potato half for a Mexican twist.

*Nutrition Boost: Substitute sour cream with Greek yogurt. Yogurt is a good source of calcium, which is needed for strong bones and teeth.

*Quick Fix: Use store-bought, pre-made bacon bits.

Chicken Cruncher Salad

Chicken Ingredients:
- 2 large boneless chicken breasts (12 ounces cooked)
- ¼ cup finely chopped pecans
- 6 tablespoons cornflake crumbs
- ¼ cup crushed Honey Bunches of Oats® cereal with almonds
- 1 teaspoon garlic salt
- ½ cup fat free milk
- ¼ cup Egg Beaters®
- ¼ cup whole wheat flour
- ⅛ cup all-purpose white flour
- Cooking spray

Salad Ingredients:
- 10 cups chopped romaine lettuce
- 1 cup finely diced celery
- 6 tablespoons low fat crumbled blue cheese
- ½ cup dried cranberries
- 2 cups mandarin oranges, canned in light syrup and drained

Dressing Ingredients:
- 2 tablespoons Newman's Own® light balsamic dressing

Directions:
1: Pound each chicken breast to about ½-inch thick. (We recommend wrapping chicken in plastic wrap and using a kitchen mallet.)
2: Combine pecans, cornflake crumbs, crushed cereal and garlic salt into shallow bowl. Combine milk and Egg Beaters® into another shallow bowl. Combine flours into a third shallow bowl.
3: Spray large skillet with cooking spray and preheat on medium heat.
4: Dip chicken into flour mixture, then into egg mixture, and finally, into breading mixture, to fully coat chicken. Then place chicken in skillet.

5: Flip chicken over as needed to fully cook, until there is no pink in chicken.
6: Ideally, let chicken cool, and refrigerate for at least 2 hours. Cut into pieces.
7: Top lettuce with celery, cheese, cranberries, oranges and chicken.
8: Serve balsamic vinaigrette dressing on the side.

Makes 5 servings.

*Lighten Up: Substitute ¼ cup pecans with another ¼ cup of crushed Honey Bunches of Oats® cereal with almonds.

*Switch It Up: Use a different low fat salad dressing.

*Nutrition Boost: Use fresh baby spinach for half of the romaine lettuce. Spinach is a power house of vitamins and minerals. Spinach contains choline and inositol, the substances that help prevent atherosclerosis, or thickening and hardening of the arteries. It is also an anti-aging vegetable.

*Quick Fix: Use pre-cooked chicken strips.

Chicken Cruncher Salad

	TGI Friday's® Pecan-Crusted Chicken Salad without Dressing (Add 590 calories w/ dressing)	Chicken Cruncher Salad
Calories	750	288
Total Fat	50g	9.2g
Sat. Fat	0g	3.2g
Fiber	0g	5g
Sugar	38g	8.2g
Protein	62g	21.8g

Berry-licious Lemon Freeze

	TGI Friday's® Strawberry Lemonade Slush (8 oz)	Berry-licious Lemon Freeze
Calories	220	150
Total Fat	*	0.5g
Sat. Fat	*	0.1g
Fiber	*	4.1g
Sugar	*	18.6g
Protein	*	3g

* Nutrition facts for this item were unavailable.

Berry-licious Lemon Freeze

Ingredients:
- 1 (16-ounce) bag frozen unsweetened strawberries
- 1 cup fat free milk
- 1 packet Cool Splashers® Vanilla
  (found in grocery store by Crystal Light® single mixes)
- 1 teaspoon lemon juice
- 1 cup ice
- ¼ cup raw sugar
- ¼ cup Cool Whip Free®, for topping

Directions:
1: Add first 6 ingredients to blender, and mix. Pour into glasses.
2: Top each with 2 tablespoons Cool Whip Free®.

Makes 4 servings.

*Lighten Up: Substitute Splenda® for sugar.

*Switch It Up: Substitute strawberries with frozen raspberries for a raspberry lemon freeze.

*Nutrition Boost: Add a banana to increase the fiber and potassium.

*Quick Fix: Make up an extra batch; freeze and re-blend for next time.

Fast Food Dinner

Fast Food Dinner

Pizza Hut® Menu Makeover

	Pizza Hut® Dinner 6" Personal Pan Pizza® Supreme, 2 Cheese Sticks, 2 Cinnamon Sticks, (2 oz icing), Sierra Mist® (22 oz)	Pizza Hut® Better Choice 6" Personal Pan Pizza® Veggie Lovers, Bistro Salad (without dressing), Cinnamon Sticks (2 oz icing), Diet Pepsi® (22 oz)	Menu Makeover Pita Pizza Supreme, Cheesy Sticks, Cinni Minni Sticks (2 oz cream cheese icing), Diet Sierra Mist® (22 oz)
Calories	1715	770	712
Total Fat	55g	18.5g	0.2g
Sat. Fat	21.5g	6g	0g
Fiber	7g	5g	0.8g
Sugar	134g	67g	29.3g
Protein	49g	22g	48g

Pita Pizza Supreme

	Pizza Hut® 6" Personal Pan Pizza® Supreme	Pita Pizza Supreme
Calories	720	450
Total Fat	35g	15.8g
Sat. Fat	13g (1g trans)	6.6g
Fiber	4g	6.4g
Sugar	8g	23.5g
Protein	31g	34.4g

Pita Pizza Supreme

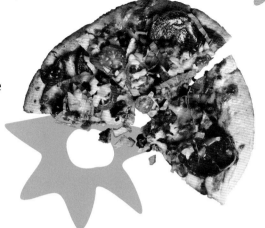

Ingredients:

- 1 whole wheat pita bread (6.5-inch diameter)
- Olive oil spray
- 2 ounces Ragu® homemade style pizza sauce
- ⅛ teaspoon garlic salt (optional)
- 7 pieces Hormel® turkey pepperoni
- 1 ounce pre-cooked turkey sausage
- 2 medium mushrooms, sliced
- 1 tablespoon onion, diced
- 1 tablespoon finely chopped bell pepper
- ½ cup low fat shredded mozzarella cheese
- Toppings of your choice, such as fresh veggies and other meats (olives, chicken and barbecue sauce, shrimp and garlic, or ham and pineapple). The options are limitless!
  * Note: Nutrition facts will change with varied toppings.

Directions:

1: Spray pita bread lightly with olive oil spray.
2: Spread top side of the pita with pizza sauce.
3: Layer with remaining ingredients, and top with additional toppings of your choice.
4: Place on oven rack or pizza stone, and bake at 375° for about 15 minutes, until cheese is golden.

*Lighten Up: Save 100 calories and 5 grams of fat by holding the sausage and pepperoni.

*Switch It Up: Have a pizza making party contest at home. Award the best tasting, most creative, healthiest, etc.

*Nutrition Boost: Throw in some additional diced pineapple. Pineapple is super high in magnesium. It also contains a substance called bromelain, which may reduce inflammation, and keep the intestinal track healthy.

*Quick Fix: Microwave instead, for about 1 to 2 minutes, until cheese is sufficiently melted. If you don't have pita bread, you can substitute ready-made Boboli® pizza crust, flat bread or an English muffin. Adjust the recipe as needed.

Cheesy Sticks

Ingredients:

- 1 ½ cups warm water
- 1 tablespoon sugar
- 1 packet rapid rise yeast
- ½ teaspoon salt
- 3 tablespoons nonfat dried milk powder
- 1 tablespoon cheddar flavored popcorn seasoning
- 2 ¼ cups all-purpose flour
- ¾ cup whole wheat pastry flour
- Cooking spray
- 1 ⅓ cups shredded fat free cheddar cheese
- 1 egg white

Directions:

1: In a large bowl, combine water, sugar and yeast. Let stand for 10 minutes or until yeast is bubbly. (Water should be warm like bath water and not too hot, or it will kill the yeast.) The sugar provides food for the yeast and is necessary. Sugar substitutes kill yeast.
2: In a separate large bowl, mix together salt, milk powder, cheddar seasoning and 1 ½ cups flour (all-purpose and whole wheat combined). Gently stir dry mixture into liquid. Gradually add the remaining flour until dough starts to pull away from the sides of the bowl, and it barely sticks to your finger. Too much flour makes the breadsticks dry.
3: Knead dough for a couple of minutes on a lightly floured surface.
4: Spray a glass or metal bowl with cooking spray, and place dough in the bowl.
5: Cover with a warm, wet towel, and let rise for 45 minutes, or until doubled in bulk.
6: Remove from bowl, and place on a lightly floured surface. Spray a baking sheet with cooking spray. Roll dough into a rectangle.
7: Top with shredded cheese, and cut into 24 strips with a pizza cutter. Gently roll each strip into a snake, and place on baking sheet.
8: Cover pan, and allow dough to rise for another 30 minutes.
9: Preheat oven to 425°. When dough has doubled in size, brush tops with egg white, and bake in oven for 12 minutes, or until golden brown.

Makes 24 breadsticks.

*Lighten Up: Substitute shredded cheddar cheese with additional cheddar popcorn seasoning, sprinkled on top.

*Switch It Up: Sprinkle tops with Parmesan cheese instead of shredded cheddar cheese.

*Nutrition Boost: Bump up the fiber by replacing 1 cup all-purpose flour with 1 cup whole wheat pastry flour.

*Quick Fix: Thaw frozen pre-made bread dough; roll, cut into sticks, top with cheese, brush with egg white, and bake.

Cheesy Sticks

	Pizza Hut® Cheese Sticks (2 breadsticks)	Cheesy Sticks (2 breadsticks)
Calories	360	155
Total Fat	14g	3.1g
Sat. Fat	7g	1.6g
Fiber	2g	1.5g
Sugar	4g	0.1g
Protein	14g	7.6g

Cinni Minni Sticks

Dough Ingredients:

- 1 ½ cups warm water
- 1 tablespoon sugar
- 1 packet rapid rise yeast
- ½ teaspoon salt
- 3 tablespoons nonfat dried milk powder
- 2 ¼ cups all-purpose flour
- ¾ cup whole wheat pastry flour
- Cooking spray
- 2 tablespoons cinnamon/sugar seasoning mix
- 1 egg white

Icing Ingredients:

- ½ cup fat free cream cheese
- ¼ cup powdered sugar
- 1 teaspoon vanilla extract

Dough Directions:

1: In a large bowl, combine water, sugar and yeast. Let stand for 10 minutes or until yeast is bubbly. (Water should be warm like bath water and not too hot, or it will kill the yeast.) The sugar provides food for the yeast and is necessary. Sugar substitutes kill yeast.
2: In a large bowl, mix together salt, milk powder and 1 ½ cups flour (all-purpose and whole wheat combined). Gently stir dry mixture into liquid. Gradually add the remaining flour until dough starts to pull away from the sides of the bowl, and it barely sticks to your finger. Too much flour makes the breadsticks dry.
3: Knead dough for a couple of minutes on a lightly floured surface.
4: Spray a glass or metal bowl with cooking spray, and place dough in the bowl.
5: Cover with a warm, wet towel, and let rise for 45 minutes or until doubled in bulk.
6: Remove from bowl, and place on a lightly floured surface. Spray a baking sheet with cooking spray. Roll dough into a rectangle, and cut into 24 strips with a pizza cutter.
7: Sprinkle cinnamon/sugar mix onto rolling surface. Roll out each piece of dough into a snake, and then drape over your forefinger and twist the dough into a spiral. Cut spiraled strip in half. Then place on baking sheet, and repeat with remaining pieces of dough. Try to space them evenly on the pan.

8: Cover pan, and allow dough to rise for another 30 minutes.

9: Preheat oven to 425°. When dough has doubled in size, brush tops with egg white, and bake in oven for 12 minutes, or until golden brown.

Icing Directions:

1: Combine all ingredients, and mix until soft and well blended.

2: Spread evenly over baked cinni sticks, while still warm.

Makes 48 breadsticks.

*Lighten Up: Substitute sugar with Splenda® for baking, and add cinnamon.

*Switch It Up: Use caramel popcorn seasoning with sugar instead of cinnamon/sugar seasoning mix.

*Nutrition Boost: Bump up the fiber by replacing 1 cup all-purpose flour with 1 cup whole wheat pastry flour.

*Quick Fix: Use pre-made Pillsbury® reduced fat breadstick dough.

Cinni Minni Sticks

	Pizza Hut® Cinnamon Sticks (2 sticks with 2 oz icing)	Cinni Minni Sticks (2 sticks with 2 oz cream cheese icing)
Calories	360	107
Total Fat	6g	0.2g
Sat. Fat	1.5g	0g
Fiber	1g	0.8g
Sugar	48g	5.7g
Protein	4g	6g

Fazoli's® Menu Makeover

	Fazoli's® Dinner Oven Baked Spaghetti with Meatballs, 2 Garlic Breadsticks, Chocolate Chip Cookie, Italian Lemon Ice with Strawberry	Fazoli's® Better Choice Small Spaghetti Marinara with Meat Sauce, 1 Breadstick, Side Garden Salad with Fat Free Italian Dressing, Chocolate Chip Cannolis	Menu Makeover Strawberry Lemon Freeze, Spectacular Spaghetti with Meatballs, Bing Bang Breadsticks, Monster Chocolate Chip Cookies
Calories	1970	865	868
Total Fat	79g	21g	7g
Sat. Fat	38g	8.5g	2.7g
Fiber	12g	15g	19.9g
Sugar	124g	17g	24.3g
Protein	52g	34g	53g

Strawberry Lemon Freeze

	Fazoli's® Italian Lemon Ice with Strawberry	Strawberry Lemon Freeze
Calories	270	0
Total Fat	0g	0g
Sat. Fat	0g	0g
Fiber	0g	0g
Sugar	70g	0g
Protein	0g	0g

Strawberry Lemon Freeze

Ingredients:
- 1 single serve packet of Crystal Light®
- 1 cup ice
- 1 cup water

Directions:
1: Combine all ingredients into blender.
2: Blend on high until consistency is smooth.

Makes 1 glass.

*Lighten Up: Zero calories! Can't get any lighter than that!

*Switch It Up: Try different flavors of Crystal Light®.

*Nutrition Boost: Add 2 to 4 frozen strawberries.

*Quick Fix: Skip the blender, and pour over ice.

Spectacular Spaghetti with Meatballs

Meatball Ingredients:

- 1 pound 99% lean ground turkey
- ¾ cup Fiber One® original bran cereal, crushed
- 1 teaspoon Italian seasoning
- 1 teaspoon garlic salt
- ½ cup egg substitute
- ¼ cup tomato paste (⅓ of a 6-ounce can)
- Cooking spray

Meatball Directions:

1: Mix ingredients together well; form into 1-inch balls and fry.
2: Spray 12-inch skillet with cooking spray. Cook meatballs in skillet over medium heat for 8 to 10 minutes, turning occasionally, until browned. Drain, if necessary.

Pasta Ingredients:

- 1 (8-ounce) package 100% whole wheat pasta of your choice: angel hair, spaghetti, linguine, rotini, penne or macaroni
- Water, for pasta

Pasta Directions:

1: Cook and drain pasta as directed on package.

Sauce Ingredients:

- 10 ounces tomato paste (1 can plus the remainder of the first 6-ounce can used in meatballs)
- 1 (14.5-ounce) can Del Monte® diced tomatoes with basil, garlic and oregano
- ¼ cup each diced green, red and yellow bell peppers
- 1 cup each sliced fresh mushrooms and diced zucchini
- ½ cup diced onion
- 4 cloves fresh garlic, crushed

Sauce Directions:
1: Mix all ingredients in a large mixing bowl.
2: Add sauce to skillet; turn browned meatballs to coat.
3: Cover; cook over medium-low heat for 15 to 20 minutes, occasionally stirring sauce and turning meatballs, until meatballs are thoroughly cooked.
4: Serve meatballs and sauce over pasta, and enjoy this filling meal!

Makes 3 servings.

*Lighten Up: Add extra veggies to the sauce: diced tomato, onion, mushroom, zucchini, peppers, etc.

*Switch It Up: For a "spicy meatball," add ¼ teaspoon ground red pepper (cayenne) to meatball mixture. Try different pasta shapes.

*Nutrition Boost: Add more vegetables! By adding more vegetables, you will naturally lower your calories, and increase your vitamin and mineral intake significantly. A whole cup of most vegetables contains less than 40 calories.

*Quick Fix: Buy pre-made sauce, and add pre-cut vegetables.

Spectacular Spaghetti with Meatballs

	Fazoli's® Oven Baked Spaghetti with Meatballs	Spectacular Spaghetti with Meatballs
Calories	890	495
Total Fat	39g	2.3g
Sat. Fat	20g	0.2g
Fiber	7g	16.9g
Sugar	13g	18.5g
Protein	41g	46g

Bing Bang Breadsticks

Ingredients:
- 1 ½ cups warm water
- 1 tablespoon sugar
- 1 packet rapid rise yeast
- ½ teaspoon salt
- 3 tablespoons nonfat dried milk powder
- 2 ¼ cups all-purpose flour
- ¾ cup whole wheat pastry flour
- Cooking spray
- 1 tablespoon I Can't Believe It's Not Butter® pump spray
- 1-2 tablespoons minced garlic
- 1 egg white

Directions:
1: In a large bowl, combine water, sugar and yeast. Let stand for 10 minutes or until yeast is bubbly. (Water should be warm like bath water and not too hot, or it will kill the yeast.) The sugar provides food for the yeast and is necessary. Sugar substitutes kill yeast.
2: In a large bowl, mix together salt, milk powder and 1 ½ cups flour (all-purpose and whole wheat flour combined). Gently stir dry mixture into liquid. Gradually add the remaining flour until dough starts to pull away from the sides of the bowl, and it barely sticks to your finger. Too much flour makes the breadsticks dry.
3: Knead dough for a couple of minutes on a lightly floured surface.
4: Spray a glass or metal bowl with cooking spray, and place dough in the bowl.
5: Cover with a warm, wet towel, and let rise for 45 minutes or until doubled in bulk.
6: Remove from bowl, and place on a lightly floured surface. Spray a baking sheet with cooking spray. Roll dough into a rectangle, and cut into 24 strips with a pizza cutter.
7: Gently roll each piece of dough into a rounded stick. Place on baking sheet, and repeat with remaining pieces of dough. Try to space them evenly on the pan.
8: Mix butter spray and minced garlic; then brush over tops of dough sticks.
9: Cover pan, and allow dough to rise for another 30 minutes.
10: Preheat oven to 425°.
11: When dough has doubled in size, brush tops with egg white, and bake in oven for 12 minutes, or until golden brown.

Makes 24 breadsticks.

*Lighten Up: Stick to only one serving, and increase your portion of vegetables or fruit.

*Switch It Up: Top breadsticks with Parmesan cheese, and chop in 2 fresh garlic cloves.

*Nutrition Boost: Replace ¼ cup all-purpose flour with soy or whole wheat flour to increase the fiber, which will keep you feeling fuller longer.

*Quick Fix: Use pre-made Pillsbury® reduced fat breadsticks, instead of making dough from scratch.

Bing Bang Breadsticks

	Fazoli's® Garlic Breadsticks (2 sticks)	Bing Bang Breadsticks (2 sticks)
Calories	300	137
Total Fat	14g	0.7g
Sat. Fat	3g	0.1g
Fiber	2g	1.9g
Sugar	2g	1.1g
Protein	6g	6g

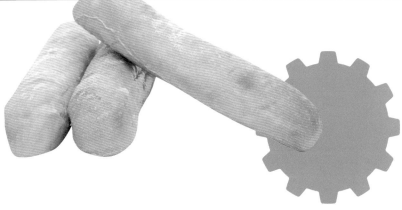

Monster Chocolate Chip Cookies

Ingredients:

- 3 tablespoons unsalted butter, melted
- 1 cup unbleached all-purpose flour
- ½ cup wheat flour
- ½ teaspoon baking soda
- ½ teaspoon table salt
- 1 cup packed light brown sugar
- ¼ cup baby food prune purée
- ¼ cup egg substitute
- 1 tablespoon vanilla extract
- ¼ cup sugar free, fat free vanilla instant pudding
- ½ cup mini chocolate chips

Directions:

1: Adjust oven rack to middle position, and heat oven to 350°. Line 2 baking sheets (or 1 big insulated sheet) with parchment paper.
2: Melt butter in small saucepan over medium heat, until color turns light brown, for about 4 minutes.
3: Whisk flours, baking soda and salt in medium bowl. In separate bowl, with electric mixer on medium speed, beat melted butter, brown sugar and prune purée until blended. Beat in egg substitute and vanilla until combined. Add pudding and dry ingredients, and mix on low speed until just combined. Stir in chocolate chips by hand.
4: Place cookies about the size of a ping-pong ball on baking sheet. Flatten cookies by hand for thinner dough, if crispier cookies are desired.
5: Bake cookies 1 sheet at a time, until edges are light golden brown and centers are soft and puffy, for 11 to 13 minutes.

Makes 16 servings.

*Lighten Up: Leave out the butter, and add an additional 3 tablespoons prune purée.

*Switch It Up: Add ¼ cup cocoa powder, and replace chocolate chips with white chocolate chips or mini M&M's®.

*Nutrition Boost: Replace ½ cup all-purpose flour with dry oatmeal, and mix in 2 tablespoons flax seed and ¼ cup nuts, to boost the fiber and omega-3 fatty acids in this recipe.

*Quick Fix: To whip up a quick batch of soft cookies, mix together ½ cup egg substitute, ½ cup prune purée, ½ cup mini chocolate chips, and 1 box of your favorite flavor of cake mix. Bake at 350° for 8 to 10 minutes.

Monster Chocolate Chip Cookies

	Fazoli's® Chocolate Chip Cookie (4 oz)	Monster Chocolate Chip Cookies (4 oz)
Calories	510	170
Total Fat	26g	4.3g
Sat. Fat	15g	2.4g
Fiber	3g	1.4g
Sugar	39g	5.6g
Protein	5g	2.4g

Manchu Wok® Menu Makeover

	Manchu Wok® Dinner	Manchu Wok® Better Choice	Menu Makeover
	General Tso's Chicken, Vegetable Egg Roll, Seafood Rangoons, Fried Rice, Coke® (24 oz)	Chicken with Snow Peas, Vegetable Egg Roll, Garlic Green Beans, Diet Coke® (24 oz)	"Go For It" General Tso's Chicken, Rock-n-Egg Rolls, Crazy Good Crab Rangoons, Foolem' Fried Rice, Diet Coke® (24 oz)
Calories	1811	494	694
Total Fat	108.2g	31g	18.7g
Sat. Fat	17.6g	4g	3.5g
Fiber	5.2g	5g	7.5g
Sugar	109.6g	9g	17.1g
Protein	47g	13g	47.1g

"Go For It" General Tso's Chicken

	Manchu Wok® General Tso's Chicken (5 oz)*	"Go For It" General Tso's Chicken (5 oz)
Calories	360	310
Total Fat	21g	10.3g
Sat. Fat	3.5g	1.4g
Fiber	1g	2.3g
Sugar	12g	11.8g
Protein	14g	29.5g

* A small order is 19.5 ounces, which is approximately 4 (5-ounce) servings.

"Go For It" General Tso's Chicken

Ingredients:

- ¼ cup whole wheat flour
- 2 chicken breasts (6 ounces each), cut into chunks
- 1 packet Sun Bird® General Tso's seasoning mix
- ⅛ cup Splenda® for baking
- 4 tablespoons reduced sodium soy sauce
- 1 ¼ cups water

- 2 tablespoons canola oil
- 1 cup shredded carrots
- 1 cup snap peas
- ½ cup canned, sliced water chestnuts, drained
- ½ cup finely chopped celery
- ¼ cup finely chopped red bell pepper

Directions:

1: Add flour to gallon sized sealable plastic food bag. Add chicken chunks; seal and shake to coat chicken.
2: Combine seasoning, Splenda®, soy sauce and water. Blend and set aside.
3: Heat oil in skillet over medium heat, and then add flour-coated chicken. Cook until evenly browned.
4: Stir sauce mixture, and add to skillet with carrots, snap peas, water chestnuts, celery and red bell pepper.
5: Bring to a boil, reduce heat, and simmer to desired consistency.

Makes 4 servings. Serve atop ½ cup of our Fried Rice. See recipe on page 121.

*Lighten Up: Use half the amount of chicken, and add 1 cup sugar snap peas.

*Switch It Up: Substitute chicken with shrimp.

*Nutrition Boost: Add 1 cup chopped broccoli.

*Quick Fix: Use 1 package frozen steamer bag Asian vegetable mix in place of fresh carrots, snap peas and peppers. Use Bird's Eye® Steam Fresh whole grain brown rice, which is even easier than making instant rice.

Rock-n-Egg Rolls

Egg Roll Ingredients:

- ⅔ cup coarsely chopped celery
- 1 can water chestnuts, drained
- ⅔ cup coarsely chopped carrot
- 1 cup bean sprouts
- 2 cups shredded cabbage
- Nonfat cooking spray
- ⅔ cup chopped onion

- ½ teaspoon minced fresh ginger
- 1 garlic clove, minced
- 2 tablespoons low-sodium soy sauce
- ¼ teaspoon black pepper
- 14 egg roll wrappers
- 1 large egg white

Sauce Ingredients:

- ¾ cup water
- 2 teaspoons cornstarch
- ⅓ cup seasoned rice vinegar
- ¼ cup brown sugar

- 1 ½ tablespoons reduced sodium soy sauce
- 1 tablespoon fresh ginger
- 2 cloves garlic, crushed
- ½ teaspoon crushed red pepper flakes

Egg Roll Directions:

1: Preheat oven to 425°.
2: Combine celery, water chestnuts and carrot in food processor, and pulse 10 times or until finely chopped.
3: In a medium bowl, combine celery mixture, bean sprouts and cabbage. Cover with plastic wrap, leaving a small corner open to vent. Microwave on high for 5 minutes. After cooking, drain any excess water.
4: Spray a skillet with nonfat cooking spray, and place over medium-high heat. Add onion, ginger and garlic; sauté for 5 to 7 minutes. Remove from heat; stir in cabbage mixture, soy sauce and pepper. Cover and place in fridge for 15 minutes.
5: Take out 1 egg roll wrapper, and set it out on a clean counter with 1 corner pointing toward you (wrapper should look like a diamond). Trim 1 inch off right and left corners of wrapper. Spoon 3 tablespoons filling into center of wrapper. Fold lower corner of egg roll wrapper over filling. Fold in trimmed corners. Moisten top corner of wrapper with egg white, and roll up. Repeat procedure with remaining wrappers.

6: Lightly coat egg rolls with cooking spray and place, seam-side-down, on a baking sheet coated with cooking spray. Bake at 425° for 18 minutes, or until golden brown.

Sauce Directions:

1: Whisk together all the ingredients in a small saucepan.
2: Bring to a boil, whisking all the while, until it thickens.
3: Remove from heat, and cool to room temperature. Serve on the side with egg rolls.

Makes 14 egg rolls.

*Lighten Up: Appetizers can be an easy way for excess calories to slip in. Keep your helpings down by filling up on steamed vegetables, fresh fruit, or flavored water. Remember to enjoy your meal by slowing down and enjoying each bite.

*Switch It Up: Add pre-cooked grilled chicken, or your favorite lean meat to the egg roll mix.

*Nutrition Boost: Mix in ¼ cup chopped avocado and ¼ cup pine nuts for half of the bean sprouts. These are high in essential fats, good for healthy skin and clear thinking.

*Quick Fix: Morningstar Farms® makes a microwavable vegetarian buffalo wing. It is located in the freezer section at most grocery stores.

Rock-n-Egg Rolls

	Manchu Wok® Vegetable Egg Rolls (1 roll)	Rock-n-Egg Rolls (1 roll)
Calories	150	75*
Total Fat	6g	0.3g
Sat. Fat	1g	0g
Fiber	1g	1.3g
Sugar	0g	1.1g
Protein	4g	3.5g

* Dipping sauce adds 16 calories.

Crazy Good Crab Rangoons

	Manchu Wok® Seafood Rangoons (3 oz)	Crazy Good Crab Rangoons (3 pieces - 3 oz)
Calories	300	168
Total Fat	21g	6.9g
Sat. Fat	7g	2.1g
Fiber	1g	0g
Sugar	3g	1.8g
Protein	4g	10.2g

Crazy Good Crab Rangoons

Ingredients:
- 1 (6-ounce) can white crabmeat
- 4 ounces light cream cheese, softened
- ¼ cup green onions, thinly sliced
- ¼ cup light mayonnaise
- 1 clove garlic, minced
- Canola oil cooking spray
- 16 wonton wrappers
- I Can't Believe It's Not Butter® pump spray

Directions:
1: Preheat oven to 350°.
2: Mix crab, cream cheese, green onions, mayonnaise and garlic together.
3: Spray cooking sheet generously with canola oil spray.
4: Place wonton wrappers flat onto baking sheet.
5: Place a rounded teaspoonful of crab mixture in the center of each wonton.
6: Spray your fingers with canola oil spray, and pinch the corners of each wrap together at the top.
7: When all wontons are completed, lightly spray them with canola oil spray.
8: Spray each wonton with 2 to 3 sprays of spray butter.
9: Bake for 20 minutes. Let cool for 3 to 5 minutes.

Optional: For 60 calories, serve with 2 tablespoons La Choy's® sweet and sour sauce.

Makes 16 rangoons.

*Lighten Up: Substitute light cream cheese with fat free cream cheese.

*Switch It Up: Add 1 diced, cooked shrimp to each rangoon before cooking.

*Nutrition Boost: Mix ½ cup puréed cauliflower into cream cheese.

*Quick Fix: Use 1 teaspoon onion powder in place of green onions.

Foolem' Fried Rice

	Manchu Wok® Fried Rice (8 oz serving)	Foolem' Fried Rice (8 oz serving)
Calories	410	141
Total Fat	13g	1.2g
Sat. Fat	2.5g	0g
Fiber	1g	3.9g
Sugar	3g	2.4g
Protein	10g	3.9g

Foolem' Fried Rice

Ingredients:

- 1 ½ cups instant brown rice, cooked
- 1 cup fat free chicken broth
- ½ cup finely diced celery
- 1 cup frozen peas and carrots
- 13 cloves garlic, minced
- 3 green onions, chopped
- 1 packet Sunbird® Fried Rice seasoning mix
- 2 tablespoons soy sauce
- 1 ½ cups raw cauliflower, grated
- ½ cup Egg Beaters®

Directions:

1: Prepare instant brown rice as directed.
2: In a large pan, add chicken broth, celery, peas, carrots, garlic and onions. Sauté over medium heat until tender.
3: Stir in seasoning mix and soy sauce.
4: Add cooked rice and cauliflower, and continue to stir until thoroughly heated.
5: Push mixture to one side of the pan, and pour Egg Beaters® on the opposite side. Cook until egg sets.
6: Stir egg into rice until evenly mixed, and serve.

Makes 6 servings.

*Lighten Up: Substitute all rice with shredded cauliflower.

*Switch It Up: Add chicken or shrimp. Use white rice instead of brown.

*Nutrition Boost: Add 1 cup chopped bok choy. Bok choy contains glucosinolates, which may be important for your immune system and may help prevent cancer.

*Quick Fix: Freeze some to use next time.

Long John Silver's® Menu Makeover

	Long John Silver's® Dinner Battered Fish (2 pc), Coleslaw, 2 Hushpuppies, Pecan Pie, Water	Long John Silver's® Better Choice 1 Grilled Tilapia, Rice, Vegetable Medley, Corn Cobbette without Butter, Water	Menu Makeover "Flippin'" Fish, Hoosier Hush Potato Pups, Cool Like Coleslaw, Maple Pecan Pie, Water
Calories	1210	430	456
Total Fat	67g	8.5g	15.9g
Sat. Fat	13.5g	2.5g	3.9g
Fiber	7g	8g	7.5g
Sugar	32g	11g	14.6g
Protein	31g	30g	26.7g

"Flippin'" Fish

	Long John Silver's® Battered Fish (2 pc)	"Flippin'" Fish (2 pc)
Calories	520	120
Total Fat	32g	2.8g
Sat. Fat	8g	1g
Fiber	0g	3.5g
Sugar	0g	0g
Protein	24g	21g

"Flippin'" Fish

Ingredients:

- Canola oil cooking spray
- ¼ cup crushed Fiber One® original bran cereal
- ½ teaspoon garlic salt
- ¼ teaspoon pepper
- 2 pieces of tilapia (3.5 ounces each)
- 1 ounce skim milk
- Lemon wedge (optional)

Directions:

1: Preheat oven to 350°.
2: Spray cooking sheet with canola oil spray.
3: Mix cereal, garlic salt and pepper together in a shallow bowl.
4: Dip fish into milk, and then into cereal mixture, until evenly coated.
5: Bake the fish for 15 to 18 minutes, or until fish is cooked through. The time depends on thickness of the fillets. Fish will flake easily with a fork when done.
6: Garnish with lemon wedge, if desired.

Makes 1 serving.

*Lighten Up: Skip the breading. Flavor with lemon pepper, and bake.

*Switch It Up: Use any type of fresh or frozen fish you like.

*Nutrition Boost: Add some ground flax seed to the breading.

*Quick Fix: Make extra, and freeze to use next time.

Hoosier Hush Potato Pups

	Long John Silver's® Hushpuppies (2 puppies)	Hoosier Hush Potato Pups (2 pups)
Calories	120	72
Total Fat	5g	2.5g
Sat. Fat	1g	1.5g
Fiber	2g	1g
Sugar	2g	0.5g
Protein	2g	4g

Hoosier Hush Potato Pups

Ingredients:

- 2 medium red potatoes, skinned, boiled and mashed
- 1 small red onion, diced
- ½ cup 2% shredded cheddar cheese
- ¼ cup Parmesan cheese, grated
- Salt, to taste
- Pepper, to taste
- ¼ cup panko bread crumbs
- ¾ cup cornflakes, powdered to bread crumb consistency (for coating)

Directions:

1: Preheat oven to 350°.
2: In a bowl, add the mashed potatoes and all of the remaining ingredients, except cornflakes.
3: Mix gently, and form nice bite-sized balls.
4: In a plate, spread the coarse cornflakes, and roll the balls to coat evenly.
5: Place them in a foil-lined tray, and bake for 30 minutes. Serve with reduced sugar or sugar free ketchup.

Makes 16 "pups."

*Lighten Up: Use fat free cheddar cheese in place of 2% shredded cheddar cheese, and replace 1 medium potato with 1 cup cooked, mashed cauliflower.

*Switch It Up: For an alternative flavor, use seasoned bread crumbs in place of panko crumbs, or add 2 tablespoons dried or fresh parsley.

*Nutrition Boost: Use sweet potatoes in place of red potatoes! Did you know one sweet potato contains 262% of your daily vitamin A needs! How's that for a super food!?

*Quick Fix: Use frozen mashed potatoes.

Cool Like Coleslaw

Ingredients:

- 1 ½ cups shredded green or red cabbage
- ½ cup grated carrots
- 3 tablespoons plain low fat yogurt
- 1 tablespoon apple cider vinegar
- 1 tablespoon Dijon mustard
- ½ teaspoon salt
- ¼ teaspoon pepper
- 3 tablespoons light Hellmann's® olive oil mayonnaise
- 1 teaspoon Splenda®

Directions:

1: Mix all ingredients well, chill, and serve.

Makes 4 servings.

*Lighten Up: Use fat free mayonnaise.

*Switch It Up: Add some hot sauce to spice it up.

*Nutrition Boost: Add 1 cup finely diced apples. Apples contain only 80 calories, and are packed full of vitamins. Did you know that apples float because 25% of their volume is air?

*Quick Fix: Buy slaw and carrots pre-shredded.

Cool Like Coleslaw

	Long John Silver's® Coleslaw (4 oz)	Cool Like Coleslaw (4 oz)
Calories	200	61
Total Fat	15g	4g
Sat. Fat	2.5g	0.7g
Fiber	3g	1g
Sugar	10g	1.9g
Protein	1g	1.2g

Maple Pecan Pie

Crust Ingredients:
- 10 (14" x 9") sheets fresh phyllo pastry or frozen pastry, thawed
- Cooking spray

Layer 1 Ingredients:
- 1 (15-ounce) can yams (sweet potatoes), drained and mashed, or 1 cup fresh
- ⅓ cup Egg Beaters®
- ¼ cup packed light brown sugar
- 1 teaspoon ground cinnamon
- ¼ teaspoon ground nutmeg
- ¼ teaspoon cloves

Layer 2 Ingredients:
- ¾ cup Egg Beaters®
- ⅓ cup dark corn syrup
- ⅓ cup light pancake syrup
- ½ cup brown sugar
- 2 teaspoons vanilla extract
- ½ cup Grape Nuts® cereal
- ¼ cup old-fashioned oats
- ⅔ cup pecans, chopped

Directions:
1: Preheat oven to 350°.
2: Prepare crust by thawing phyllo dough in the refrigerator for at least an hour before assembling the crust. Once thawed, place stack of phyllo sheets on a piece of wax paper. Cover the top with a wet paper towel to prevent drying/cracking. Take one sheet off the top, and place in a 9-inch pie dish, spraying both the top and bottom. Continue layering phyllo sheets, spraying both sides, until all 10 sheets have been used. Top the sheets of phyllo by placing corners just to the right of the previous sheet's corners. Bake until lightly browned, for about 10 minutes.

3: In a mixing bowl, blend together the Layer 1 ingredients. Spread evenly on bottom of pie crust.

4: In a mixing bowl, beat together the first 5 ingredients in Layer 2, until mixture is frothy. Stir in Grape Nuts®, oats and half of the pecans. Carefully spoon over yam layer. Top with the rest of the pecans.

5: Cover edges of pie crust with aluminum foil to prevent a burnt crust! Bake for 50 to 60 minutes or until filling is set around edges, or until a knife inserted halfway between the center and edge comes out clean. Cool and serve.

Makes 10 servings.

*Lighten Up: Use all sugar free syrup, and replace yams with 1 can of pumpkin.

*Switch It Up: Add a colorful twist to this pie by spreading 1 cup chopped fresh or frozen cranberries on top of the phyllo dough crust before adding the first layer mixture.

*Nutrition Boost: Add ¼ cup whole flax seeds with the Grape Nuts® and oats. Flax seed is Alpha Linolenic Acid, a type of omega-3 fatty acid that may help lower blood pressure, triglycerides, unhealthy cholesterol, cancer risk, and help with irritable bowel.

*Quick Fix: Skip the pie crust, and use a trans fat free pre-made graham cracker crust.

Maple Pecan Pie

	Long John Silver's® Pecan Pie	Maple Pecan Pie
Calories	370	203
Total Fat	15g	6.6g
Sat. Fat	2g	0.7g
Fiber	2g	2g
Sugar	20g	12.2g
Protein	4g	0.5g

KFC® Menu Makeover

	KFC® Dinner Chicken Pot Pie, Coleslaw, Corn Bread Muffin, Miranda® Strawberry (20 oz)	KFC® Better Choice Grilled Chicken Drumstick and Thigh, Green Beans (20 oz), 3" Corn on the Cob, Mashed Potatoes w/o Gravy, Tropicana® Sugar Free Lemonade	Menu Makeover Power Packed Pot Pie, Corny Muffins, Cool Like Coleslaw, Crystal Light® Orange (16 oz)
Calories	1360	420	413
Total Fat	60g	18.5g	8.2g
Sat. Fat	34.5g	4g	2.7g
Fiber	7g	4g	5.4g
Sugar	118g	2g	10.1g
Protein	31g	32g	25.2g

Power Packed Pot Pie

	KFC® Chicken Pot Pie (13 ounces)	Power Packed Pot Pie
Calories	690	272
Total Fat	40g	3.8g
Sat. Fat	31g	1.8g
Fiber	3g	3.3g
Sugar	14g	4g
Protein	27g	21.3g

Power Packed Pot Pie

Ingredients:

- 4 cups instant mashed potato flakes
- 1 teaspoon garlic salt
- 2 teaspoons Butter Buds® sprinkles
- ½ teaspoon onion powder
- 1 cup skim milk
- 4 cups water, divided
- Canola oil spray

- 12 ounces boneless, skinless chicken breast
- 1 (10 ¾-ounce) can 98% fat free condensed cream of chicken soup
- 1 (12-ounce) bag Bird's Eye® Steam Fresh frozen mixed vegetables (peas, carrots, corn and green beans), thawed
- ½ teaspoon pepper

Directions:

1: Preheat oven to 375°.
2: Combine potato flakes, garlic salt, Butter Buds®, onion powder, milk and 3 cups hot water. Mix well.
3: Spread half of mixture evenly over the bottom of a pre-sprayed, 3-quart rectangular baking dish. Bake alone for 15 to 20 minutes.
4: Spray skillet with cooking spray. Dice chicken, and place in skillet on medium to high heat. Stir occasionally and cook, until there is no pink in chicken.
5: In a large mixing bowl, combine cooked chicken, soup, 1 cup water, thawed mixed vegetables and pepper. Mix well.
6: Spread soup and vegetable mixture evenly over the potato layer.
7: Using a large spoon and the remaining potato mixture, drop 6 spoonfuls separately over the top.
8: Bake uncovered for 30 to 40 minutes. Let stand for 5 minutes before serving.

Makes approximately 6 (13-ounce) servings.

*Lighten Up: Cut the chicken to 9 ounces, and add 3 more ounces of vegetables.

*Switch It Up: Change the chicken breast to turkey breast for a turkey pot pie!

*Nutrition Boost: Substitute half of the instant potatoes with cooked sweet potatoes.

*Quick Fix: Use pre-cooked, diced, packaged chicken.

Corny Muffins

Ingredients:

- 1 cup flour
- 1 cup cornmeal
- 1 teaspoon baking soda
- ½ teaspoon salt
- ⅓ cup sugar

- 1 cup fat free yogurt
- ½ cup egg substitute
- ¼ cup honey
- ¼ cup corn
- Cooking spray

Directions:

1: Preheat oven to 400°.
2: In a medium mixing bowl, combine dry ingredients.
3: Stir in yogurt, egg substitute, honey and corn.
4: Pour into 9" x 13" pan, sprayed with cooking spray (or use a cast iron skillet).
5: Bake for approximately 20 minutes.
6: Best served warm.

Makes 20 servings.

*Lighten Up: Watch out for high calorie condiments, such as butter, jelly and maple syrup. Use fat free spray butter or sugar free jams and syrup. If you prefer stick butter, keep the serving light. 1 teaspoon (the size of a postage stamp) contains 40 calories. One serving of baby carrots, about the size of a baseball, has the same amount of calories!

*Switch It Up: Add 1 chopped jalapeno pepper, ¼ cup chopped bell pepper and ½ cup shredded 2% or fat free cheddar cheese.

*Nutrition Boost: Replace ½ cup yogurt with ½ cup sweet potato puréed baby food.

*Quick Fix: Preheat oven to 350°. Mix 1 box corn muffin mix with ¼ cup egg substitute, ⅓ cup skim milk, ½ cup sugar, and 1 (8-ounce) can creamed corn. Pour in a sprayed 9" x 13" pan, and bake for 30 minutes.

Corny Muffins

	KFC® Cornbread Muffins (1 muffin)	Corny Muffins (1 muffin)
Calories	210	80
Total Fat	9g	0.4g
Sat. Fat	1.5g	0.2g
Fiber	1g	1.1g
Sugar	11g	4.2g
Protein	3g	2.7g

Cool Like Coleslaw

Add Cool Like Coleslaw to complete this meal. See recipe on page 126.

	KFC® Cole Slaw (4.5 oz)	Cool Like Coleslaw (4 oz)
Calories	180	61
Total Fat	11g	4g
Sat. Fat	1.5g	0.7g
Fiber	2g	1g
Sugar	14g	1.9g
Protein	1g	1.2g

Restaurant Dinner

Don Pablo's® Menu Makeover

	Don Pablo's® Dinner Cheese Quesadilla (small - 4 slices), 12 Chips & Salsa, Lemonade, Kid's Small Fried Ice Cream	Don Pablo's® Better Choice Mama's Skinny Enchiladas (3 enchiladas), Mexican Rice, Seasoned Vegetables, Water, with Lemon	Menu Makeover "Forget the Fried" Ice Cream, Quickest Quesadillas, Tiki Tonga Tropical Salsa & Classic Chips, Crystal Light® Lemonade (16 oz)
Calories	1768	671	868
Total Fat	67g	20g	20.6g
Sat. Fat	20g	6g	6.6g
Fiber	8g	10g	30.1g
Sugar	120.7g	9g	52.8g
Protein	48g	29g	30.9g

"Forget the Fried" Ice Cream

	Don Pablo's® Fried Ice Cream Kid's Size	"Forget the Fried" Ice Cream
Calories	424	278
Total Fat	18g	3.5g
Sat. Fat	10g	1.1g
Fiber	1g	5g
Sugar	28g	30g
Protein	6g	6.7g

"Forget the Fried" Ice Cream

Ingredients:

- ½ cup Fiber One® Caramel Delight cereal, crushed
- 1 cup Cinnamon Toast Crunch® cereal, crushed
- 2 cups Blue Bunny® fat free vanilla frozen yogurt
- 2 tablespoons light or sugar free caramel syrup
- ¼ cup light or fat free whipped cream

Directions:

1: Pour cereal in a plastic zip-lock bag, and crush with your hands until cereal is in large crumbles and pieces. Pour crushed cereal into a small 9" x 9" inch baking pan.
2: Scoop yogurt into 4 (½-cup) balls.
3: Roll yogurt balls into cereal until completely covered.
4: Place the pan with the yogurt balls into the freezer for about 2 hours.
5: Turn oven to broil. When the oven is ready, take the pan with the yogurt out of the freezer, and place in oven for 1 minute, until cereal is slightly brown. Watch the yogurt carefully to avoid melting.
6: Top with light or sugar free caramel syrup and whipped cream.

Makes 4 servings.

*Lighten Up: Save 50 calories by leaving out the whipped cream and caramel topping.

*Switch It Up: Use different flavors of low fat ice cream or frozen yogurt.

*Nutrition Boost: Top ice cream with hot cinnamon apples. Dice one apple, and place in microwave bowl. Add 1 Splenda® packet, 1 teaspoon cinnamon and 1 teaspoon lemon juice. Microwave for 2 to 3 minutes until soft.

*Quick Fix: Skip steps 4 and 5.

Quickest Quesadillas

Quesadilla Ingredients:

- Canola oil cooking spray
- 1 Santa Fe bean frozen dinner (Lean Cuisine® or Lean Gourmet®)
- 4 (6-inch) Mission® Carb Balance whole wheat tortillas
- 1 cup canned, diced tomatoes (Mexican version, if available)
- 1 cup 2% reduced fat shredded cheese (any variety you like)
- Seasoning to make spicy, if desired

Dip Ingredients:

- ½ cup fat free sour cream and/or taco sauce (optional)

Directions:

1: Spray quesadilla maker or skillet with cooking spray.
2: Microwave Santa Fe bean dinner as directed on box.
3: Place 1 tortilla onto cooking surface.
4: Put ½ of Santa Fe bean dinner on tortilla, and spread to about 1 inch from edge.
5: Top with ½ of the diced tomatoes and ½ of the cheese.
6: Add additional seasoning, if desired.
7: Place the second tortilla on top.
8: Close the quesadilla maker lid, and remove when ready light comes on.
9: If using a skillet, on medium heat, press top tortilla down. Cook until slightly browned, then flip over. Carefully remove tortilla when that side is slightly browned.
10: Cut into wedges with a pizza cutter.
11: Repeat with the next tortillas and remaining ingredients.
12: Optional: Serve with fat free sour cream and/or taco sauce.

Makes 2 servings.

*Lighten Up: Use fat free cheese in place of 2% cheese.

*Switch It Up: Add 2 ounces diced, cooked chicken to recipe.

*Nutrition Boost: Add ½ cup chopped bell peppers. Peppers are high in vitamin A, and also contain substances to help neutralize free radicals. Free radicals are major players in the build-up of cholesterol in the arteries that lead to atherosclerosis and heart disease, the nerve and blood vessel damage seen in diabetes, the cloudy lenses of cataracts, the joint pain and damage seen in osteoarthritis and rheumatoid arthritis, and the wheezing and airway tightening of asthma.

*Quick Fix: Buy frozen Smart Ones® Fiesta Quesadilla meal.

Quickest Quesadillas

	Don Pablo's® Cheese Quesadilla (small - 4 slices)	Quickest Quesadillas (one 6-inch quesadilla)
Calories	816	415
Total Fat	50g	11.5g
Sat. Fat	27g	5g
Fiber	2g	20.5g
Sugar	4g	9g
Protein	36g	19.5g

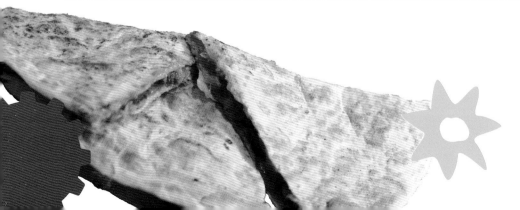

Tiki Tonga Tropical Salsa

Salsa Ingredients:

- 4 ripe medium sized tomatoes, chopped
- 2 jalapeno peppers, seeded and chopped (skip these if you don't like it "spicy")
- 1 small onion, chopped
- 4 tablespoons fresh chopped cilantro
- 1 or 2 garlic cloves, finely chopped
- 2 tablespoons fresh lime juice
- ¼ cup diced peaches
- ¼ cup diced mango

Salsa Directions:

1: Keep fingers away from face, and wear protective glasses when chopping jalapenos.
2: Combine chopped ingredients in a bowl, and, if you're not in a hurry, refrigerate for at least an hour to let the flavors mingle.

* Enjoy with Classic Chips (recipe on next page).

Makes 2.5 servings.

Tiki Tonga Salsa & Classic Chips

	Don Pablo's® Chips & Salsa	Tiki Tonga Tropical Salsa & Classic Chips
Calories	338	170
Total Fat	17g	5.6g
Sat. Fat	3g	0.5g
Fiber	5g	4.6g
Sugar	2g	13.8g
Protein	5g	4.7g

Classic Chips

Tortilla Chips Ingredients:
- 4 (6-inch) Mission® Carb Balance whole wheat tortillas
- Canola oil cooking spray
- Salt, to taste

Tortilla Chips Directions:
1: Preheat oven to 400°.
2: Cut the tortillas into 8 wedges.
3: Spray cookie sheets with canola oil cooking spray.
4: Place triangles in a single layer on 2 cookie sheets.
5: Spray chips with canola oil cooking spray.
6: Sprinkle salt over chips, as desired.
7: Bake until crisp, for 10 to 15 minutes. (Best if chips are flipped over midway through cooking time.)

*Lighten Up: Replace ½ of the chips with carrot or celery slices.

*Switch It Up: Add cheddar cheese or ranch flavored popcorn seasoning to baked chips, for a flavored tortilla chip.

*Nutrition Boost: Use whole wheat pita bread or spinach tortillas instead of whole wheat tortillas for thicker, heartier and higher fiber chips.

*Quick Fix: Use store-bought baked tortilla chips.

Buffalo Wild Wings® Menu Makeover

	Buffalo Wild Wings® Dinner Boneless Wings & Traditional Wings Combo Platter (12 wings, fries, celery, slaw, and bleu cheese), ½ Order Mozzarella Sticks, Coke® (32 oz)	Buffalo Wild Wings® Better Choice Naked Tenders (6 piece) with Sweet BBQ Sauce, Cole Slaw, Kid's Ice Cream with Chocolate Sauce, Diet Coke® (32 oz)	Menu Makeover Ba Ba Ba Boom! Buffalo "Wings," Marvelous Mozzarella Sticks, Cool Like Coleslaw, "Un-fried" Fries, Celery with Light Blue Cheese Dressing (2 tbsp), Diet Coke® (32 oz)
Calories	2312	680	618
Total Fat	124g	35g	12.3g
Sat. Fat	27.5g	6g	5.7g
Fiber	9g	3g	11.3g
Sugar	115.5g	54g	21.7g
Protein	81g	13g	51.9g

Ba Ba Ba Boom! Buffalo "Wings"

	Buffalo Wild Wings® Boneless Wings & Traditional Wings Combo	Ba Ba Ba Boom! Buffalo "Wings" (½ pound)
Calories	1480	264
Total Fat	98g	1.8g
Sat. Fat	20g	0.5g
Fiber	6g	0.3g
Sugar	2g	17.9g
Protein	66g	31.8g

Ba Ba Ba Boom! Buffalo "Wings"

Ingredients:

- 3 pounds fresh chicken breasts
- 1 ½ cups reduced sugar apricot or peach preserves
- 1 (1-ounce) package dry onion soup mix
- ½ (16-ounce) bottle light Catalina salad dressing
- 1 tablespoon chili powder
- 1 teaspoon cayenne pepper
- Hot sauce, to taste

Directions:

1: Preheat oven to 350°.
2: Cut the chicken breasts into individual pieces.
3: Place chicken on a cookie sheet lined with foil. (You may need 2 cookie sheets).
4: Mix apricot preserves, dry onion soup mix, light Catalina dressing, chili powder, cayenne pepper and hot sauce together in a bowl. Pour sauce mixture over chicken. Bake in the preheated oven for 45 minutes. Flip pieces over halfway through, and continue to cook for the remainder of the time.
5: Turn heat to 400°, and bake for an additional 15 minutes.

Makes 10 servings.

*Lighten Up: Use fat free salad dressing, and use sugar free fruit preserves or purée real fruit in place of the low sugar preserves.

*Switch It Up: Use light Red Russian dressing in place of light Catalina, or try using different low sugar fruit preserves for a different taste!

*Nutrition Boost: Serve "wings" with a side of celery and carrot sticks.

*Quick Fix: Morningstar Farms® makes a microwavable vegetarian buffalo wing. It is located in the freezer section at most grocery stores.

Marvelous Mozzarella Sticks

Ingredients:

- ½ cup Fiber One® cereal, crushed
- 1 teaspoon Italian seasoning, depending on your seasoning preference
- ¼ teaspoon garlic salt (optional)
- Salt and pepper, to taste (optional)
- 3 mozzarella string cheese sticks (2% reduced fat)
- ¼ cup egg substitute
- Canola oil cooking spray

Directions:

1: Preheat oven to 375°.
2: In a food processor, or by hand, crush cereal until bread crumb consistency.
3: Mix crumbled cereal, Italian seasoning, garlic salt, and salt and pepper in a lidded, plastic container.
4: Cut each mozzarella stick lengthwise in half, and then in half widthwise, making a total of 12 pieces.
5: Pour egg substitute into a shallow container. Place mozzarella sticks in egg substitute to coat all sticks.
6: Put coated cheese sticks into container with cereal crumbs and seasoning.
7: Cover container with lid securely, and shake until cheese sticks are covered with seasoned cereal crumb mixture.
8: Place cheese sticks on a pre-sprayed baking sheet, and place in oven for 10 minutes.

* Great with Newman's Own® Marinara sauce as a dip.

Makes 2 servings.

*Lighten Up: Decrease the amount of cheese by half, and melt into 1 cup puréed cauliflower. Let cool, and gently roll into stick shapes. Dip in egg mixture, and roll in breading mixture. Bake as previously directed.

*Switch It Up: Add panko bread flakes in place of Fiber One® for a crunchier stick.

*Nutrition Boost: Add a tablespoon of finely chopped fresh parsley to egg mixture. 1 tablespoon parsley is a good source of vitamin K, vitamin A, folic acid, vitamin C, potassium and fiber. It also has a high flavonoid content, making it a powerful antioxidant.

*Quick Fix: Just use Italian seasoned bread crumbs for the breading.

Marvelous Mozzarella Sticks

	Buffalo Wild Wings® Mozzarella Sticks (6 sticks)	Marvelous Mozzarella Sticks (6 sticks)
Calories	560	165
Total Fat	22g	7.3g
Sat. Fat	15g	4.5g
Fiber	0g	7g
Sugar	2g	0.3g
Protein	30g	15.4g

Cool Like Coleslaw

Add Cool Like Coleslaw to complete this meal. See recipe on page 126.

	Buffalo Wild Wings® Slaw (3 oz)	Cool Like Coleslaw (4 oz)
Calories	170	61
Total Fat	15g	4g
Sat. Fat	0g	0.7g
Fiber	3g	1g
Sugar	6g	1.9g
Protein	0g	1.2g

Add "Un-fried"Fries to complete this meal. See recipe on page 43.

"Un-fried" Fries

	Buffalo Wild Wings® Fries (6 oz)	"Un-fried" Fries (4.9 oz)
Calories	570	128
Total Fat	30g	0.2g
Sat. Fat	5g	0g
Fiber	7g	3g
Sugar	0g	1.6g
Protein	3g	3.5g

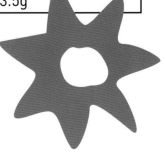

Lone Star Steakhouse® Menu Makeover

	Lone Star Steakhouse® Dinner	Lone Star Steakhouse® Better Choice	Menu Makeover
	Chopped Steak, 2 Dinner Rolls, Mac and Cheese, ½ Order Spinach & Artichoke Dip and Chips, Baked Potato w/ Honey Butter, ½ Order Big Brownie Blast, Coke® (24 oz)	Caesar Salad with Grilled Chicken with Light Italian Dressing, Baked Potato, Steamed Vegetables, Apple Cobbler, Diet Coke® (24 oz)	Champion Chopped Steak, Roll On Over, "Moving It" Mac & Cheese, Spectacular Spinach Artichoke Dip & Classic Chips, Baked Potato (8.2 oz), Spray Butter, Brownie-Ala-Yum, Diet Coke® (24 oz)
Calories	3786	915	1071
Total Fat	191.3g	26.7g	25.5g
Sat. Fat	78.4g	8.1g	4.2g
Fiber	18.6g	22.4g	9.8g
Sugar	247.6g *	59.3g	47.1g
Protein	111.4g	55.1g	52.4g

* Nutrition fact for Spinach & Artichoke Dip was unavailable.

Champion Chopped Steak

	Lone Star Steakhouse® Chopped Steak (12 oz)	Champion Chopped Steak
Calories	900	306
Total Fat	70.8g	11g
Sat. Fat	28.8g	2g
Fiber	0g	0.5g
Sugar	0g	2.2g
Protein	60g	27.8g

Champion Chopped Steak

Steak Ingredients:

- 1 egg, beaten
- 1 tablespoon Worcestershire sauce
- ¼ cup finely chopped onion
- ½ cup chopped mushrooms
- ½ cup quick oats
- 1 (6-ounce) can tomato paste
- ½ teaspoon garlic salt
- ¼ teaspoon pepper
- 1 pound Laura's Lean® 96% ground beef
- Cooking spray

Sauce Ingredients:

- 1 package McCormick® mushroom gravy mix
- 1 cup cold water
- 1-2 cups chopped mushrooms

Directions:

1: In a large bowl, combine all steak ingredients except ground beef and cooking spray, and mix well.
2: Crumble beef over mixture, and mix well.
3: Shape into 4 equal patties.
4: Spray skillet with cooking spray, and cook on medium-high heat, flipping over as needed until cooked as desired.
5: In a separate small saucepan, start with mushroom gravy mix, and add water gradually, stirring into gravy mix with whisk. Then add mushrooms.
6: Stir frequently; cook on medium heat until gravy comes to boil. Reduce heat, and simmer for 1 minute. (Gravy will thicken upon standing.)
7: Spoon sauce over steak, and serve.

Makes 4 (12-ounce) servings.

*Lighten Up: Add ¼ cup diced green peppers to meat mix, and make into 6 smaller servings.
*Switch It Up: Add hot sauce and chili powder to meat mixture for a spicier version.

*Nutrition Boost: Add 1 (6-ounce) can of tomato paste.

*Quick Fix: Microwave gravy. Stir water into gravy mix in 1 ½ quart microwavable bowl. Microwave on HIGH 2 to 3 minutes, or until thickened, stirring after each minute. Microwave ovens vary; cook time is approximate.

Roll On Over

	Lone Star Steakhouse® Dinner Roll (2 rolls)	Roll On Over (2 rolls)
Calories	732	202
Total Fat	15.5g	4g
Sat. Fat	11.2g	0g
Fiber	4.6g	4g
Sugar	67.4g	1.2g
Protein	20.2g	6.6g

Roll On Over

Ingredients:

- 1 packet rapid rise yeast
- ½ cup warm water
- 1 tablespoon sugar
- 1 cup mashed, cooked sweet potato
- 2 tablespoons canola or olive oil
- ¾ teaspoon salt
- 1 egg, slightly beaten
- 1 ½ cups whole wheat pastry flour
- 3 tablespoons Splenda®
- 2 cups bread flour
- Nonfat cooking spray

Directions:

1: Dissolve yeast, warm water and 1 tablespoon sugar in a mixing bowl. Let stand for 5 minutes.
2: Meanwhile, mix mashed sweet potato, oil, salt and slightly beaten egg in a large bowl. Stir in yeast mixture, and mix well. Stir in wheat flour, Splenda® and bread flour until smooth. Shape into a ball, and cover bowl. Let rise about 20 minutes, or place in fridge overnight.
3: Spray muffin tins with nonfat cooking spray. Scoop out dough, and place in muffin tins. If dough was not refrigerated overnight, allow to rise for an additional 20 minutes or until doubled.
4: Bake at 375° for 12 to 20 minutes. Serve warm.

Makes 20 rolls.

*Lighten Up: Keep your portions under control by placing just one roll on your plate, and putting the rest in the freezer, or away from the table.

*Switch It Up: In place of sweet potatoes, use ½ of an 8-ounce can of crushed pineapple and ½ cup pineapple juice.

*Nutrition Boost: Top rolls with apple butter or applesauce to boost your vitamin C.

*Quick Fix: To make 5 quick rolls, mix 1 cup self-rising flour, ½ cup skim milk and 2 tablespoons light ranch dressing in a bowl. Pour in a muffin pan, and bake at 350° for 15 minutes.

"Moving It" Mac & Cheese

	Lone Star Steakhouse® Macaroni and Cheese (3 oz)	"Moving It" Mac & Cheese (3 oz)
Calories	187	85
Total Fat	9g	1.5g
Sat. Fat	5.7g	0.1g
Fiber	0.6g	0.7g
Sugar	4g	1g
Protein	7.7g	5g

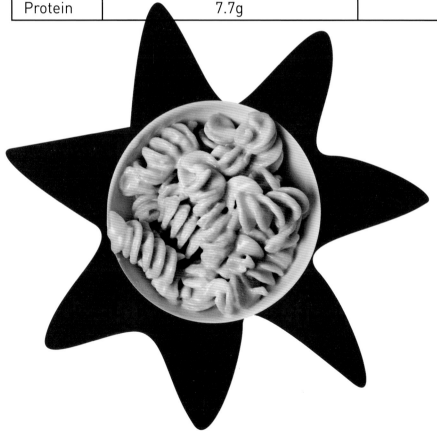

"Moving It" Mac & Cheese

Ingredients:

- 2 quarts water
- 1 cup dry Barilla Plus® macaroni
- ¾ cup skim milk
- 2 ounces Velveeta® 2% cheese
- 2 teaspoons white cheddar flavored popcorn seasoning
- ¼ cup fat free sour cream
- 5 sprays I Can't Believe It's Not Butter® pump spray

Directions:

1: Bring water in saucepan to a boil. Add macaroni. Cook and stir occasionally, until noodles are soft.
2: Preheat oven to 350°.
3: Drain noodles in a colander.
4: Reduce heat to low, and pour noodles back into pan.
5: Add milk, cheese, white cheddar seasoning and sour cream; stir until cheese has melted.
6: Put into a 1 ½ quart casserole dish. Spray top with butter pump spray.
7: Bake for 15 minutes, until top is golden brown.

Makes 4 servings.

*Lighten Up: Use fat free cheese.

*Switch It Up: Use sharp cheddar cheese flavored popcorn seasoning instead of white cheddar. It will taste more like a boxed macaroni and cheese, which some kids prefer.

*Nutrition Boost: Add ½ cup of puréed cooked cauliflower into cheese sauce.

*Quick Fix: Make extra to freeze, and use later.

Spectacular Spinach Artichoke Dip & Classic Chips

	Lone Star Steakhouse® Spinach & Artichoke Dip (10.8 oz) and ½ Order Chips	Spectacular Spinach Artichoke Dip (5.1 oz) & Classic Chips (approximately 10 chips)
Calories	438	251
Total Fat	31.2g	8.4g
Sat. Fat	12.3g	1.8g
Fiber	4g	3.2g
Sugar	*	4.5g
Protein	9.4g	10.7g

* Nutrition fact for this item was unavailable.

Spectacular Spinach Artichoke Dip

Ingredients:

- 1 (9-ounce) box frozen chopped spinach, thawed
- 1 (14-ounce) can artichoke hearts, drained
- 1 cup fat free sour cream
- ½ cup reduced fat grated Parmesan cheese
- 1 cup shredded fat free mozzarella cheese, divided
- 8 ounces fat free cream cheese, softened
- 4 cloves garlic, crushed
- ½ teaspoon freshly ground black pepper, plus more as needed
- 1 tablespoon hot horseradish sauce - add to desired taste

Directions:

1: Preheat oven to 350°.
2: Thaw spinach in advance or in the microwave; drain and squeeze as much liquid as possible from spinach.
3: Open artichoke can, and drain.
4: Add all ingredients, except ½ cup mozzarella cheese, into a large bowl. Mix well, using a large spoon.
5: Place in a 1-quart baking dish.
6: Top with remaining mozzarella cheese.
7: Bake until bubbly, for about 30 minutes. Enjoy with our Classic Chips! See recipe on page 141.

Makes 2 servings (10.2 ounces).

*Lighten Up: Cut down the portion size to make three 3.5-ounce servings.

*Switch It Up: Substitute artichokes with a 6-ounce can crab meat.

*Nutrition Boost: Add more spinach.

*Quick Fix: Cook in the microwave, instead of using the oven.

Brownie-Ala-Yum

Brownie Ingredients:

- 1 cup sugar
- ½ cup flour
- ¼ cup whole wheat flour
- ½ cup Hershey's® unsweetened cocoa powder
- 1 ½ teaspoons vital wheat gluten*

- 2 teaspoons cornstarch
- ¼ teaspoon baking soda
- ¼ teaspoon salt
- 1 (6-ounce) container nonfat yogurt
- Nonstick cooking spray

Topping Ingredients:

- 6 tablespoons low sugar chocolate syrup
- Fat free Blue Bunny® vanilla frozen yogurt
- 2 tablespoons fat free whipped cream
- 1 cherry

Directions:

1: Preheat oven to 350°.
2: Mix all dry ingredients.
3: Add yogurt, and mix well. Batter will be very thick.
4: Spray an 8" x 8" pan with nonstick cooking spray, and spread batter evenly.
5: Bake for 30 to 35 minutes.
6: When brownie cools, top with topping ingredients.

Makes 12 large brownies.

* Vital wheat gluten helps bind ingredients to provide a chewy texture. It can be found in the baking aisle of grocery stores, near the flour.

*Lighten Up: Leave off the frozen yogurt, and use double the fat free whipped cream serving.

*Switch It Up: Top with berries.

*Nutrition Boost: Mix in ½ cup mashed, canned beans, rinsed and drained.

*Quick Fix: Use No Pudge® brownie mix in place of brownie recipe.

Brownie-Ala-Yum

	Lone Star Steakhouse® Big Brownie Blast (½ serving)	Brownie-Ala-Yum (with ½ cup Blue Bunny® Frozen Yogurt)
Calories	695	227
Total Fat	34.5g	0.6g
Sat. Fat	15g	0.3g
Fiber	4g	1.4g
Sugar	85g	38.2g
Protein	8g	2.3g

Chili's® Menu Makeover

	Chili's® Dinner ½ Skillet Queso with Chips, Steak & Portobello Fajita with 3 Flour Tortillas, Sweet Shot Double Fudge Brownie, Dr. Pepper® (24 oz)	Chili's® Better Choice Guiltless Chicken Platter, Side Salad with Lowfat Ranch Dressing, Cup of Southwestern Vegetable Soup, Mandarin Oranges, Diet Coke® (24 oz)	Menu Makeover Steam'n Steak Fajitas with 3 Corn Tortillas, No Quack Queso & Classic Chips, Double Decker Fudge Swirl Cups, Diet Dr. Pepper® (24 oz)
Calories	2350	795	705
Total Fat	126.5g	21g	18.9g
Sat. Fat	40.5g	8.5g	7.4g
Fiber	25g	12g	26.2g
Sugar	151g	100g	18g
Protein	61.5g	54g	38.9g

Steam'n Steak Fajitas

	Chili's® Steak & Portobello Fajita with 3 Tortillas (does *not* include condiments)	Steam'n Steak Fajitas (including 3 tortillas)
Calories	1170	287
Total Fat	66g	8.9g
Sat. Fat	11.5g	3.9g
Fiber	9g	4.6g
Sugar	21g	1.7g
Protein	56g	18.5g

Steam'n Steak Fajitas

Ingredients:

- 1 pound thinly sliced, boneless flank steak
- ¼ cup beef broth
- 1 large onion, sliced
- 1 large green bell pepper, sliced
- 1 large red bell pepper, sliced
- 2 cups portobello mushrooms, sliced
- 1-2 cloves garlic, minced
- ¼ cup water
- 1 package McCormick® fajita seasoning mix
- 1 tablespoon chili powder
- 20 (6-inch) corn tortillas (3 tortillas per serving)
- 2 ½ cups Weight Watchers® Mexican blend shredded cheese (2 tablespoons per fajita)
- 2 cups tomatoes, diced
- Hot sauce, to taste
- Optional toppings: fat free or light sour cream, taco sauce, lettuce

Directions:

1: Spray skillet, and preheat on medium-high heat.
2: Add meat, cook and stir until no longer pink.
3: Remove meat, and add ¼ cup broth.
4: Add onion, peppers, mushrooms and garlic. Cook for 5 to 10 minutes.
5: Return meat to skillet.
6: Stir in water, seasoning mix and chili powder.
7: Stir, and cook another 5 to 10 minutes.
8: Spoon into warm tortillas. Top with 2 tablespoons cheese, diced tomatoes, hot sauce, and any other additional toppings desired. Wrap tortilla up, and enjoy.

Makes approximately 7 servings.

*Lighten Up: Use fat free cheese.

*Switch It Up: Substitute beef with chicken.

*Nutrition Boost: Add some eggplant! Cut a fresh eggplant into cubes, place in a microwave-safe dish, cover, and cook for 3 to 5 minutes until tender.

*Quick Fix: Use pre-cooked, packaged meat.

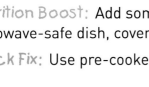

No Quack Queso & Classic Chips

	Chili's® Skillet Queso & Chips (½ skillet)	No Quack Queso & Classic Chips (12 Chips with ½ cup Queso Sauce)
Calories	460	298
Total Fat	36.5g	9.1g
Sat. Fat	15g	3.1g
Fiber	15g	10.8g
Sugar	0g	4.8g
Protein	4.5g	16.9g

No Quack Queso & Classic Chips

Ingredients:

- 2 tablespoons cornstarch
- ½ cup cold water
- ½ cup skim milk
- 4 ounces Velveeta® cheese
- 4 tablespoons canned, diced tomatoes and green chiles

Directions:

1: Mix cornstarch with ½ cup cold water, and mix well. Set aside.
2: Mix remaining ingredients in a small saucepan, and heat over medium-high heat until melted.
3: Add cornstarch mixture, and stir constantly.
4: Bring to a boil, and reduce heat. Let simmer, and stir constantly, until thickened. Serve with our Classic Chips! See recipe on page 141.

Makes 2 (½-cup) servings.

*Lighten Up: Substitute half of the Velveeta® cheese with fat free cheese.

*Switch It Up: Add hot sauce to make it hotter!

*Nutrition Boost: Add ½ cup diced bell peppers.

*Quick Fix: Skip the cornstarch and water. Combine a full cup skim milk with cheese, tomatoes and chiles. Microwave and stir until evenly melted. (This won't be as thick as the original recipe.)

Double Decker Fudge Swirl Cups

Ingredients:

- 1 ½ cups whole wheat flour
- 1 teaspoon salt
- 1 teaspoon baking powder
- 2 ¼ cups raw sugar
- 1 ¼ cups cocoa
- 4 teaspoons instant coffee powder

- 1 (15-ounce) can black beans
- 1 tablespoon vanilla
- 1 cup water
- 1 (8-ounce) container Cool Whip Free®
- 24 (5-ounce) clear Dixie® cups

Directions:

1: Preheat oven to 350°.
2: Combine all the dry ingredients.
3: Drain a can of black beans, and rinse thoroughly until the water runs clear. Return the black beans back to the can, and fill with water.
4: Dump beans and water in a food processor or blender, and purée until smooth.
5: Add the purée to the dry mix, along with vanilla and the extra cup of water. Stir to combine.
6: Pour the batter into a greased 9" x 13" pan. Bake for 25 to 30 minutes, rotating the pan around, halfway through. When the brownies are finished baking, they should be firm in the center, and the edges should be slightly puffy and starting to pull away from the sides. It's important not to overbake in the oven, because they will keep baking once you take them out.
7: Let brownies cool completely. Cut into 48 (1x1-inch) squares.
8: Place 1 square in a Dixie® cup, add 1 tablespoon Cool Whip Free®, add another brownie square, and finish with 1 tablespoon Cool Whip Free®.
9: Repeat for all Dixie® cups.

Makes 24 servings.

*Lighten Up: Substitute a layer of brownie with sliced fruit.

*Switch It Up: In place of regular Cool Whip Free®, try chocolate or strawberry flavored Cool Whip® Dips.

*Nutrition Boost: Add a ½ serving of calcium by replacing Cool Whip Free® with 1 (4-ounce) container of vanilla pudding.

*Quick Fix: Use a No Pudge® brownie mix.

Double Decker Fudge Swirl Cups

	Chili's® Sweet Shot Double Chocolate Fudge Brownie	Double Decker Fudge Swirl Cups (1 cup)
Calories	420	120
Total Fat	24g	0.9g
Sat. Fat	14g	0.4g
Fiber	1g	3.2g
Sugar	50g	11.5g
Protein	1g	3.5g

Olive Garden® Menu Makeover

	Olive Garden® Dinner	Olive Garden® Better Choice	Menu Makeover
	Fettuccine Alfredo, Garden Fresh Salad with Dressing, 2 Breadsticks, Black Tie Mousse Cake, Raspberry Lemonade	Minestrone Soup, Salad without Dressing, 1 Breadstick, Linguine Alla Marinara, Sundae, Diet Coke®	Lemon Razz-a-Ma-Tazz, Fabulous Fettuccine Alfredo, Guilt-Free Garden Salad, Bing Bang Breadsticks, Chocolate Cake Supreme
Calories	2850	830	746
Total Fat	153g	19.5g	8.3g
Sat. Fat	79.5g	7.5g	3.5g
Fiber	8g	15g	8.1g
Sugar	131g	31g	30.5g
Protein	63.5g *	31.5g	25.8g

* Nutrition fact for Garden Fresh Salad was unavailable.

Lemon Razz-a-Ma-Tazz

	Olive Garden® Raspberry Lemonade (2 glasses)	Lemon Razz-a-Ma-Tazz (2 glasses)
Calories	220	10
Total Fat	0g	0g
Sat. Fat	0g	0g
Fiber	0g	0g
Sugar	58g	0g
Protein	0g	0g

Lemon Razz-a-Ma-Tazz

Ingredients:

- 1 tub Crystal Light® raspberry lemonade mix
- 2 quarts water
- 1 can diet lemon-lime soda or Sprite Zero®

Directions:

1: Mix one tub of Crystal Light® raspberry lemonade mix into 2 quarts water, and stir.
2: Mix in diet lemon-lime soda or Sprite Zero®.
3: If desired, garnish with fresh orange slices.

Makes four (16-ounce) servings.

*Lighten Up: Go for a glass of water instead.

*Switch It Up: Use a different drink mix flavor. You can also pour the mixture into a popsicle mold or several Dixie® cups, add a wooden popsicle stick, and freeze until set.

*Nutrition Boost: Add ½ cup fresh or frozen raspberries. Raspberries are one of the highest fiber fruits, and are also high in ellagic acid, a phenolic compound that may help prevent cancer, inhibit the growth of cancer cells, and stop the growth of some cancers.

*Quick Fix: Buy pre-made bottled Crystal Light®.

Fabulous Fettuccine Alfredo

Sauce Ingredients:

- 2 cups skim milk
- ½ cup low fat buttermilk
- ¼ cup fat free half & half
- ½ cup grated Parmesan cheese
- ½ cup 2% shredded mozzarella cheese
- 1 tablespoon I Can't Believe It's Not Butter® pump spray
- 1 tablespoon minced garlic
- ½ teaspoon salt
- ¼ teaspoon pepper

Sauce Directions:

1: Heat all ingredients in a saucepan over medium heat.
2: Reduce to low heat, and continue stirring frequently for about 10 minutes, as sauce thickens.

Pasta Ingredients:

- 5-6 quarts water
- 1 tablespoon salt
- 12 ounces Barilla Plus® fettuccine noodles

Pasta Directions:

1: Bring 5 to 6 quarts of water and 1 tablespoon salt to a boil in an 8-quart pot.
2: Place all of the noodles in boiling water.
3: Continue to cook and stir frequently for approximately 13 minutes, and then drain well. Once sauce and noodles are cooked, spoon sauce over noodles.

Makes 6 servings (about 1 cup cooked pasta and 3.3 ounces sauce per serving).

*Lighten Up: Replace half of fettuccine noodles with cooked spaghetti squash. If you are unfamiliar with spaghetti squash, it is a fun vegetable that looks just like spaghetti noodles when cooked and scooped out of the outer skin.

*Switch It Up: Add chicken or shrimp.

*Nutrition Boost: Microwave a steamable bag of mushrooms and broccoli (or your favorite veggie combination), and mix into the pasta. Top with sauce. Mushrooms have been popular from ancient times. The Pharaohs considered them a delicacy, while the Romans called them "gifts of the gods." Mushrooms are brimming with protein, B vitamins and minerals (selenium, potassium and copper). They're also low in calories!

*Quick Fix: Make an extra batch to freeze, and use for next time.

Fabulous Fettuccine Alfredo

	Olive Garden® Fettuccine Alfredo (dinner portion)	Fabulous Fettuccine Alfredo (1 serving)
Calories	1220	284
Total Fat	75g	5.5g
Sat. Fat	47g	2.8g
Fiber	5g	6g
Sugar	5g	2.5g
Protein	37.5g	15.5g

Guilt-Free Garden Salad

	Olive Garden® Garden Fresh Salad with Dressing	Guilt-Free Garden Salad (with 2 tablespoons dressing)
Calories	350	117
Total Fat	26g	1.6g
Sat. Fat	4.5g	0g
Fiber	3g	9.5g
Sugar	10g	6.8g
Protein	*	4.3g

* Nutrition fact for this item was unavailable.

Add Bing Bang Breadsticks to complete this meal. See recipe on page 110.

Bing Bang Breadsticks

	Olive Garden® Breadsticks (2 sticks)	Bing Bang Breadsticks (2 sticks)
Calories	300	137
Total Fat	4g	0.7g
Sat. Fat	1g	0.1g
Fiber	0g	1.9g
Sugar	3g	1.1g
Protein	10g	6g

Guilt-Free Garden Salad

Salad Ingredients:

- 2 cups mixed salad greens
- ½ cup shredded or chopped carrots
- ¼ cup chopped celery
- ¼ cup chopped jicama
- ½ cup chopped or sliced tomatoes
- 2 tablespoons apples, diced
- 2 tablespoons original Fiber One® cereal

Salad Directions:

1: Wash all vegetables well.
2: Cut vegetables up to desired size.
3: Place vegetables in bowl.
4: Top with Fiber One® and Red Lava dressing (directions below).

Makes 1 serving of salad.

Red Lava Dressing Ingredients:

- ¾ cup tomato juice
- ¼ cup balsamic vinegar or red wine vinegar
- 1 envelope Italian salad dressing mix
- 2 teaspoons sugar

Red Lava Dressing Directions:

1: In a jar with a tight-fitting lid, combine all ingredients; shake well. Store in the refrigerator.

Makes 8 servings of dressing (2 tablespoons/serving).

*Lighten Up: Stay away from extra salad toppings, such as bacon bits and croutons, as these items can easily pack on extra calories if you use more than 1 to 2 tablespoons.

*Switch It Up: Use a different light salad dressing.

*Nutrition Boost: Top with sugar snap peas and fruit, such as berries and mandarin oranges. Both fruits and sugar snap peas are rich in vitamin C, a vitamin essential to healing cuts and wounds.

*Quick Fix: Put together the salad from the grocery store salad bar.

Chocolate Cake Supreme

Layer 1 Ingredients:
- 1 box No Pudge® brownie mix
- ⅔ cup nonfat yogurt
- Cooking spray

Layer 1 Directions:
1: Prepare No Pudge® brownies as directed, adding nonfat yogurt, as well. Pour batter into sprayed sheet cake pan. Bake as directed on box. Let cool.

Layer 2 Ingredients:
- 2 single serve containers sugar free, fat free chocolate pudding

Layer 2 Directions:
1: Spread pudding over brownie layer.

Layer 3 Ingredients:
- 1 cup Diet Coke®
- 1 cup devil's food cake mix

Layer 3 Directions:
1: Mix Diet Coke® and devil's food cake mix, and pour into another sprayed sheet cake pan. Bake for about 10 minutes, or until inserted toothpick comes out clean.
2: Let cool, or place in freezer for 20 minutes to prevent breakage when removing from pan.
3: Remove cake layer from pan, and carefully place over pudding layer.

Frosting Ingredients:
- 1 (8-ounce) container Cool Whip Free®
- 2 tablespoons unsweetened Hershey's® cocoa powder

Frosting Directions:
1: Mix cocoa powder with Cool Whip Free®, and spread evenly on top of cake.
2: Cover and store in refrigerator.

Makes 12 servings.

*Lighten Up: Split the dessert with someone special.

*Switch It Up: Drizzle with sugar free caramel syrup.

*Nutrition Boost: Top with fruit to get an extra boost of fiber. All fruits have natural cancer-fighting compounds, and also help boost your immune system.

*Quick Fix: Skip the No Pudge® brownie layer, and mix a 12-ounce can of Diet Coke® with 1 package of chocolate cake mix. Bake in sprayed sheet cake pan for about 10 minutes until done. Top cake with Chocolate Cool Whip Dips®.

Chocolate Cake Supreme

	Olive Garden® Black Tie Chocolate Mousse Cake	Chocolate Cake Supreme
Calories	760	222
Total Fat	48g	2g
Sat. Fat	27g	0.5g
Fiber	0g	0.4g
Sugar	65g	23.5g
Protein	9g	2.9g

Denny's® Menu Makeover

	Denny's® Dinner Homestyle Meatloaf with Gravy, Mashed Potatoes, Apple Crisp a la mode, Root Beer Float	Denny's® Better Choice Tilapia Rancheros (19 oz), Mashed Potatoes, Green Beans, Chocolate Pudding	Menu Makeover "Move Over Meat" Loaf, Creamy Cauli-Mash, Cinni-Sweet Zucchini Treats, Float On Overs
Calories	1950	795	503
Total Fat	91g	26.5g	8.8g
Sat. Fat	36g	7.5g	1.9g
Fiber	5g	11g	6.5g
Sugar	159g	25g	25.3g
Protein	48g	61g	21.2g

"Move Over Meat" Loaf

	Denny's® Homestyle Meatloaf with Gravy (7 oz)	"Move Over Meat" Loaf (7 oz)
Calories	600	165
Total Fat	46g	3.8g
Sat. Fat	17g	0.5g
Fiber	0g	2.1g
Sugar	4g	5.9g
Protein	33g	12g

"Move Over Meat" Loaf

Meatloaf Ingredients:

- 2 packages Morningstar Farms® Meal Starters™ Sausage Style Recipe Crumbles
- 1 cup onion, chopped
- 1 cup shredded carrots
- 1 cup chopped baby bella mushrooms
- ½ cup egg substitute
- 1 tablespoon Worcestershire sauce
- 1 teaspoon salt

- ⅓ teaspoon pepper
- 1 teaspoon ground sage
- 1 teaspoon garlic powder
- 2 teaspoons mustard
- 1 tablespoon vegetable oil
- 3 ½ slices whole wheat bread, cubed
- ⅓ cup fat free milk
- 1 (8-ounce) can tomato sauce

Tangy Glaze Ingredients:

- ½ cup ketchup
- 1 teaspoon mustard

- 1 tablespoon brown sugar

Directions:

1: Preheat oven to 350°.
2: In a large bowl, combine crumbles, onion, shredded carrots, egg substitute, mushrooms, Worcestershire sauce, salt, pepper, sage, garlic powder, oil, mustard, bread cubes, milk and tomato sauce. Transfer to a 9" x 13" baking dish; form into a loaf. Mix Glaze ingredients; pour on top.
3: Bake for 60 to 90 minutes. Let stand 15 minutes before slicing.

Makes 9 servings.

*Lighten Up: Substitute brown sugar in Glaze with Splenda® brown sugar.

*Switch It Up: Make meatloaf cupcakes by spooning meatloaf mixture in paper cupcake liners, and bake in cupcake pan at 350° for 30 to 40 minutes. Top meatloaf cupcakes with mashed potatoes or our Creamy Cauli-Mash recipe on page 175!

*Nutrition Boost: Adding more soy protein in your diet, and eating less animal protein, has been shown to help lower LDL or "bad" cholesterol. A recent study found that those consuming 2 servings of soy a day had an 8% lower risk of colorectal cancer.

*Quick Fix: Use ¾ cup whole wheat bread crumbs in place of sliced bread.

Creamy Cauli-Mash

	Denny's® Mashed Potatoes	Creamy Cauli-Mash
Calories	170	85
Total Fat	7g	3.8g
Sat. Fat	1g	1.4g
Fiber	1g	2.4g
Sugar	1g	0g
Protein	2g	3.7g

Creamy Cauli-Mash

Ingredients:

- 1 ½ quarts water
- 4 cups cauliflower florets
- 1 cup potato, chopped
- 2 garlic cloves, minced
- 2 tablespoons Hellmann's® canola mayonnaise or a light mayo
- 2 tablespoons low fat sour cream
- ¼ cup 2% mozzarella cheese
- ¼ teaspoon each salt, white pepper and basil

Directions:

1: Bring a large pot with 1 ½ quarts water to a boil. Add the cauliflower, and cook over medium heat until completely tender, for 20 to 30 minutes.
2: While cauliflower is cooking, microwave the potato until tender.
3: Drain cauliflower in a colander. With a bowl or small plate, press on the cauliflower to remove all water. Toss the cauliflower, and continue pressing out the water.
4: In a mixing bowl or food processor, blend the cauliflower and baked potato with all remaining ingredients, until creamy.

Makes 5 servings.

*Lighten Up: Use all cauliflower, and try fat free ingredients.

*Switch It Up: For cowboy mashed potatoes, substitute 2 cups cauliflower with 2 cups cooked carrots, cheddar cheese for mozzarella, and toss in ¼ cup corn!

*Nutrition Boost: Not only does cauliflower lower the calories in this mash, it is also a good source of allicin, a substance beneficial for your heart and for reducing stroke risk. It is also a cruciferous vegetable, well-known for its cancer-fighting potential.

*Quick Fix: Steam cauliflower in microwave with ¼ cup water, until tender.

Cinni-Sweet Zucchini Treats

Ingredients:

- 1 tablespoon light Smart Balance® butter, at room temperature
- ¼ cup packed light brown sugar
- ⅓ teaspoon ground allspice or cinnamon
- 4 cups zucchini slices
- 1 teaspoon fresh lemon juice, combined with 1 tablespoon water

Topping Ingredients:

- ½ cup old-fashioned oats
- ½ cup Golden Grahams® cereal, crushed
- ½ teaspoon cinnamon
- 2 tablespoons brown sugar
- I Can't Believe It's Not Butter® pump spray

Directions:

1: In a small bowl, combine the butter, brown sugar, and allspice or cinnamon.
2: Cut zucchini into apple shaped slices.
3: Arrange the zucchini upright in a deep microwave-safe casserole dish. Pour the lemon water over the slices, and divide the sugar mixture evenly.
4: Cover the zucchini loosely with wax paper, and microwave for 6 to 8 minutes, until tender.
5: Then top with a mixture of oats, cereal, cinnamon, brown sugar and a few squirts of spray butter. Microwave for an additional 2 to 3 minutes.
6: Set aside to cool for at least 10 minutes before serving.

Makes 8 servings.

*Lighten Up: Leave out the brown sugar and butter by mixing zucchini with 2 tablespoons light orange juice, and cooking for 6 to 8 minutes in the microwave. Mix cooked zucchini with chunky applesauce, and proceed to step 4.

*Switch It Up: Give this recipe some color and extra flavor by mixing in a handful of cranberries with the zucchini.

*Nutrition Boost: This recipe can help you get your vegetable servings in for the day. Zucchini is a type of summer squash, which provides an excellent source of vitamin C. This nutrient helps heal cuts and wounds, and keeps teeth and gums healthy. Summer squash are also dietary sources of potassium and beta-carotene.

*Quick Fix: You can make a quicker version of mock apple crisp by using 2 packets of instant cinnamon sugar oatmeal, and a few squirts of spray butter. Place in microwave for 2 to 3 minutes.

Cinni-Sweet Zucchini Treats

	Denny's® Apple Crisp a la mode (1 crisp)	Cinni-Sweet Zucchini Treats (1 treat)
Calories	750	138
Total Fat	21g	1.2g
Sat. Fat	9g	0g
Fiber	4g	2g
Sugar	91g	2.4g
Protein	7g	1.5g

Float On Overs

	Denny's® Root Beer Float (16 oz)	Float On Overs (16 oz)
Calories	430	115
Total Fat	17g	0g
Sat. Fat	9g	0g
Fiber	0g	0g
Sugar	63g	17g
Protein	6g	4g

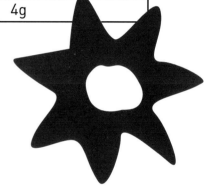

Float On Overs

Ingredients:
- 1 can diet root beer
- ½ cup Blue Bunny® nonfat vanilla frozen yogurt
- 2 tablespoons fat free spray whipped cream
- 2 cherries

Directions:
1: Scoop ½ cup frozen yogurt, and place into a large glass.
2: Pour diet root beer over frozen yogurt.
3: Top with whipped cream and cherries.

Makes 1 serving.

*Lighten Up: Mix ¼ cup light ice cream, 6 ounces diet root beer, ½ cup skim milk, ¾ cup ice cubes, 1 packet Splenda® and 1 teaspoon vanilla extract in a blender for 30 seconds.

*Switch It Up: Use nonfat mint chocolate chip ice cream in place of frozen yogurt.

*Nutrition Boost: Add extra cherries! Cherries have among the highest levels of disease-fighting antioxidants when compared to other fruits. They also contain other important nutrients, such as beta-carotene (19 times more than blueberries or strawberries), vitamin C, potassium, magnesium, iron, fiber and folate.

*Quick Fix: Make a batch of root beer float pops for a quick grab-and-go treat. Pour cold diet root beer into a pitcher, and put it in the freezer for 10 minutes until very cold, but not yet frozen. Put a cherry in each popsicle mold. Pour cold diet root beer into each mold, until it is half full. Add a small scoop of frozen yogurt into each pop mold, so it is about three-quarters full. Slowly add more root beer until the molds are full. Scoop off the foam with a spoon. Place a wooden stick in each mold. Freeze for at least 6 hours.

The Cheesecake Factory®
Menu Makeover

	The Cheesecake Factory® Dinner	The Cheesecake Factory® Better Choice	Menu Makeover
	Louisiana Chicken Pasta, ¼ Sweet Corn Tamale Cakes, Brownie Sundae Cheesecake, Strawberry Lemonade	¼ Edamame Appetizer, Shrimp with Angel Hair Pasta, ½ Fresh Strawberry Cheesecake, Iced Green Tea	Chicken Pasta Pizzazz, Cow-A-Bunga Corn Cakes (with sauces), Chewy-Gooey Brownie Cheesecake, Crystal Light® Pink Lemonade (16 oz)
Calories	3887	1297	765
Total Fat	*	*	14.3g
Sat. Fat	113g	17g	5g
Fiber	*	*	6.3g
Sugar	*	*	40g
Protein	*	*	42.1g

* Nutrition facts were unavailable.

Chicken Pasta Pizzazz

	The Cheesecake Factory® Louisiana Chicken Pasta	Chicken Pasta Pizzazz
Calories	2052	397
Total Fat	72.3g	6.3g
Sat. Fat	58g	2g
Fiber	4.2g	4.3g
Sugar	4.1g	6g
Protein	60.7g	30.4g

Chicken Pasta Pizzazz

Chicken Ingredients:

- 5 (3-ounce) chicken breasts
- ½ cup panko bread crumbs
- ½ cup seasoned bread crumbs
- 1 cup fat free mayonnaise
- Olive oil spray

Sauce Ingredients:

- 10 ounces uncooked bow tie pasta
- Salted water, for pasta
- ½ cup pre-sliced mushrooms
- ¼ cup onion, diced
- 1 small zucchini, cut in thick ½-inch circles
- ½ cup pea pods
- 1 small red bell pepper, cut into ¼-inch-thick slices
- 1 small yellow bell pepper, cut into ¼-inch-thick slices
- 2 teaspoons Cajun seasoning
- ¼ teaspoon salt
- ⅔ cup fat free half & half
- 1 (14-ounce) can fat free, less-sodium chicken broth
- 1 tablespoon chopped, fresh flat-leaf parsley
- 4 tablespoons fresh basil
- ½ cup crumbled feta or grated Parmesan cheese (your choice)
- Salt and pepper, to taste

Directions:

1: Wash and drain chicken breasts.
2: Pound until very thin (the thinner the chicken breasts, the better).
3: Mix bread crumbs together.
4: Spread a light coat of mayonnaise on chicken breasts, and cover in bread crumb mixture.

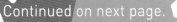
Continued on next page.

Chicken Pasta Pizzazz (con't.)

5: Spray a cookie sheet with oil, and place chicken on pan. Place in oven.

6: Bake at 375° for 30 minutes, or until golden brown.

7: Meanwhile, cook bow-tie pasta in large pot of boiling, salted water until tender, but still firm to bite. Drain, and return to pot.

8: Spray a large skillet with olive oil spray, and place over medium-high heat. Add mushrooms, onions, zucchini, pea pods and peppers. Sauté for 4 minutes.

9: Add Cajun seasoning and salt to pan; sauté for 30 seconds. Stir in fat free half & half and chicken broth.

10: Simmer until sauce reheats and thickens slightly, for about 5 minutes.

11: Add parsley, basil and cheese to sauce, stirring to incorporate.

12: Season sauce, to taste, with salt and pepper. Reduce heat to low, and let simmer until it thickens. Once it reaches desired consistency, remove from heat.

13: Place pasta with sauce on plate, and top with chicken breast.

Makes 6 servings.

*Lighten Up: Skip the breading, and top pasta with grilled or baked chicken.

*Switch It Up: For a seafood flair, top pasta with shrimp instead of chicken.

*Nutrition Boost: For a heart healthy boost, add ½ cup of edamame to the dish.

*Quick Fix: Use 1 bag of frozen vegetables in place of the fresh, whole vegetables.

Cow-A-Bunga Corn Cakes

Corn Cake Ingredients:

- ¾ cup all-purpose flour
- ½ cup cornmeal
- 1 teaspoon baking powder
- ¼ teaspoon salt
- 1 teaspoon sugar
- 1 (14 ¾-ounce) can cream-style corn
- ½ cup skim milk
- ¼ cup egg substitute
- Vegetable oil cooking spray

Corn Cake Directions:

1: In a large bowl, combine flour, cornmeal, baking powder, salt and sugar.
2: Stir well, and make a well in center of mixture.
3: In a medium bowl, combine cream-style corn, skim milk and egg substitute.
4: Add the milk mixture to the well in the flour mixture. Stir to combine, just until moistened.
5: Preheat a griddle or large skillet, and spray it with cooking spray. Working in batches if necessary, pour about 2 to 3 tablespoons of batter for each corn cake onto the hot griddle or skillet.
6: Turn the corn cakes when the tops are covered with bubbles, and the edges look cooked. Then cook on the other side until done. The skillet or griddle may need to be coated again with the cooking spray.

Makes 30 cakes (15 servings).

Continued on next page.

Cow-A-Bunga Corn Cakes (con't.)

Corn Cake Sauces:

Salsa Verde Ingredients:

- 2 tomatillos, chopped, with skins removed
- 1 (4-ounce) can mild green chiles
- 1 green onion
- 2 tablespoons fresh cilantro
- 1 ¼ teaspoons granulated sugar
- ¼ teaspoon ground cumin
- ¼ teaspoon salt
- ⅛ teaspoon ground black pepper

Southwestern Sauce Ingredients:

- ½ cup light mayonnaise
- 1 teaspoon white vinegar
- 1 teaspoon water
- ¾ teaspoon granulated sugar
- ½ teaspoon chili powder
- ¼ teaspoon paprika
- ⅛ teaspoon cayenne pepper
- ⅛ teaspoon onion powder
- 1 dash salt
- 1 dash garlic powder

Garnish Ingredients:

- ¼ cup light sour cream
- 1 (8-ounce) can tomato salsa
- ½ avocado, chopped
- 2 tablespoons fresh cilantro, coarsely chopped

Sauce Directions:

1: To prepare Salsa Verde: Combine all ingredients in a food processor on high speed. Cover and chill.
2: To prepare Southwestern Sauce: Combine all ingredients in a small bowl. Cover and chill.
3: Spoon a portion of Salsa Verde onto a plate or platter. Coat the entire plate about ¼-inch deep. Arrange the corn cakes side-by-side on the Salsa Verde.
4: Spoon a dollop of sour cream onto each corn cake.
5: Drizzle the Southwestern Sauce over the cakes in a criss-cross pattern.
6: Spoon some tomato salsa over the cakes, followed by the chopped avocado. Sprinkle with coarsely chopped cilantro leaves over the top.

*Lighten Up: Skip the Southwestern Sauce, and top corn cakes with an extra portion of tomato salsa.

*Switch It Up: Replace ¼ cup of the cream-style corn with green peas.

*Nutrition Boost: Serve corn cakes on a bed of fresh spinach. Spinach is a good source of many vitamins and minerals. It only contains 7 calories for one whole cup.

*Quick Fix: Instead of making the sauces, buy light southwestern salad dressing and salsa verde.

Cow-A-Bunga Corn Cakes

	The Cheesecake Factory® Sweet Corn Tamale Cakes (serves 4)	Cow-A-Bunga Corn Cakes (2 cakes with sauce)
Calories	371 per serving (total: 1495)	142
Total Fat	*	5g
Sat. Fat	12g per serving	1g
Fiber	*	2g
Sugar	*	4g
Protein	*	3g

* Nutrition facts for this item were unavailable.

Chewy-Gooey Brownie Cheesecake

Crust Ingredients:
- 1 package No Pudge® brownie mix, prepared according to box directions
  * May substitute with 10 ounces of brownie mix (half of a 20-ounce package), prepared with ¼ cup Egg Beaters® and 1 tablespoon water

Cheesecake Filling Ingredients:
- 1 (8-ounce) package softened light cream cheese (Neufchatel)
- 1 (8-ounce) package fat free cream cheese
- 1 cup low fat cottage cheese
- ¾ cup sugar
- 2 teaspoons vanilla extract
- 2 teaspoons lemon juice
- ¾ cup egg substitute

Topping:
- 1 tablespoon fat free or sugar free caramel topping

Directions:
1: Preheat oven to 350°. Grease the bottom of a 10-inch spring form pan.
2: In a small bowl, prepare No Pudge® brownie mix according to the directions on the box. Spread into the greased 10-inch spring form pan. Bake for 12 minutes.
3: In a large bowl, beat the cream cheeses and cottage cheese until well-mixed and smooth.
4: Add sugar, vanilla and lemon juice, and beat until well combined.
5: Add egg substitute, beating until smooth.
6: Pour cheesecake filling onto brownie crust. Bake in oven for 50 minutes, until the center is almost set. Remove from oven. Run a palette knife around the outside of the cheesecake, to allow air to circulate a little, and cool on a wire rack. Carefully remove rim of pan; then chill for at least 4 hours.
7: Top with fat free or sugar free caramel topping.

Makes 16 servings.

*Lighten Up: Replace light cream cheese and 1% cottage cheese with fat free versions.

*Switch It Up: Make a fruity cheesecake! Instead of a brownie crust, you can mix ½ cup Grape Nuts® with ¼ cup apple juice concentrate, and press into the bottom of a 9-inch spring form pan. Bake at 350° for 8 minutes, and let the crust cool before filling with cheesecake. For the cheesecake filling, add a cup of chopped fresh fruit, and increase the lemon juice to a full tablespoon.

*Nutrition Boost: Top cheesecake with a handful of fresh fruit to help you feel fuller, and increase your immune system.

*Quick Fix: Use a pre-made graham cracker crust, but check the label to make sure the crust is trans-fat free!

Chewy-Gooey Brownie Cheesecake

	The Cheesecake Factory® Brownie Sundae Cheesecake	Chewy-Gooey Brownie Cheesecake
Calories	1265	226
Total Fat	63g	3g
Sat. Fat	43g	2g
Fiber	2g	0g
Sugar	80g	30g
Protein	14g	8.7g

Menu Makeover Magic

Learning the "tricks of the trade" for healthy cooking can allow us to enjoy all of our favorite traditional recipes, fast food, and restaurant foods, without the boatloads of unhealthy consequences that accompany them. Here are some common substitutions you can use to remake your favorite dishes.

Original Recipe	Makeover Substitutions
Butter, margarine, shortening or oil in baking	Unsweetened applesauce, apple butter, mashed bananas, prune purée or canned pumpkin in place of ½ the amount called for
Butter, margarine, shortening or oil to prevent sticking	Cooking spray or nonstick pans
Butter in cooking for flavor	Butter spray, Butter Buds® or just leave out and flavor with appropriate seasonings
Butter, margarine or oil for sautéing	Cooking spray, chicken, beef or vegetable broth
Eggs	Two egg whites or ¼ cup egg substitute for each whole egg
Regular cheese	Reduced fat or fat free cheese
Regular sour cream	Reduced fat or fat free sour cream or fat free plain yogurt
Regular cream cheese	Reduced fat or fat free cream cheese, ½ cup ricotta cheese puréed with ½ cup fat free cream cheese, or puréed low fat or fat free cottage cheese
Regular mayonnaise or salad dressings	Reduced calorie or fat free dressings
Oil in oil-based marinades	Balsamic or flavored vinegars, fat free salad dressings
Evaporated milk, cream or half & half	Evaporated skim milk

Menu Makeover Magic

Original Recipe	Makeover Substitutions
Whole milk / 2% milk	Fat free milk
Creamed soups	Reduced fat creamed soup, mashed potato flakes or puréed potato or tofu
Sugar for baking	Reduce amount of sugar by 25% - 50%, use honey in about ½ the amount, or use a sugar substitute for baking like Splenda®
Sugar	Reduce amount of sugar by 25% - 50%, or use raw sugar, stevia, agave nectar, or a sugar substitute like Splenda® or Nevella®
Flour	Whole wheat flour to replace ½ the amount called for
Dry bread crumbs	Panko flakes, crushed bran cereal or rolled oats
Pastry dough	Graham cracker crumb crust
Shortening	Olive oil or Spectrum® Spread made without hydrogenated oils
Pasta	Whole grain pasta
Bacon	Turkey bacon

About The Author

Lori Walton, RN BSN

Lori Walton has been a pediatric registered nurse for more than 20 years, is the mother of two teenage girls, and was a former overweight child. These three aspects of Lori's life, along with many blessings, have given her the life experiences enabling her to empower kids and their families who are struggling to stay healthy in an unhealthy world. As the pediatric weight management coordinator for Peyton Manning Children's Hospital at St.Vincent, and director of the pediatric weight management program, L.I.F.E. (Lifetime Individual Fitness and Eating) for Kids, she works with families one-on-one to set achievable short-term goals. Once mastered, these goals are the stepping stones to lifelong healthy lifestyle habits.

One of the most effective tools Lori has found in getting kids to eat healthy is to provide healthy recipes and samples of the foods they already like, which mostly come from fast food restaurants. That is what led Lori into her most challenging project to date, *Menu Makeovers - A Playbook for Healthy Eating*. "My friends and family can attest to the fact that I am not a very good cook, do not particularly enjoy cooking, and do not choose to spend what little free time I may have in the kitchen," said Lori. "If you fit into any of these categories, have no fear, these recipes are simple and quick."

Most importantly, all of us at Project 18 hope this book will result in healthier meals for your family that even your kids will enjoy!

About The Author

Gretchen Fisher, RD CD

Gretchen Fisher is a registered dietitian at Peyton Manning Children's Hospital at St.Vincent, with a specialty in pediatric nutrition. She graduated from Indiana University with a bachelor's degree in Nutrition and Dietetics in 2005, and completed her dietetic internship at Indiana University - Purdue University at Indianapolis (IUPUI) the following year. After her internship, she completed a 10-month pediatric nutrition program at IUPUI, and is currently pursuing her master's degree in dietetics with a pediatric emphasis. Gretchen is an expert in food and nutrition, and strongly believes in the importance of a well-balanced diet for optimal mental and physical health. She loves working with children and families to help them build healthy, lifelong nutritional habits, and strives to make learning about food fun, easy and interesting. In addition to working one-on-one with families and individuals, she is a public speaker, a recipe and menu writer, and a regular participant in worksite wellness events and health fairs throughout the Indianapolis area.

Gretchen's passion for food and nutrition began at a very young age when one of her favorite toys was a play kitchen and a large collection of plastic toy food. She would spend hours preparing imaginary meals in her little toy oven. She also developed an early interest in cooking through her mother's readings of such books as *Thunder Cake* and *Stone Soup*. Eventually, she took the daring leap from playing with plastic play food to cooking with real foods, by reading the *Alpha Bakery for Children* by General Mills, a cookbook with recipes for every letter of the alphabet. These formative experiences allowed her to continue cultivating her skills and her passion for cooking, and to incorporate her nutritional expertise into creating delicious and wholesome recipes. Her hope is that this cookbook may inspire children and families in much the same way as her first cookbook inspired her. After all, we are what we eat, and all the better when we make our meals fresh, try new foods, and, most importantly, live a more nutritious life.

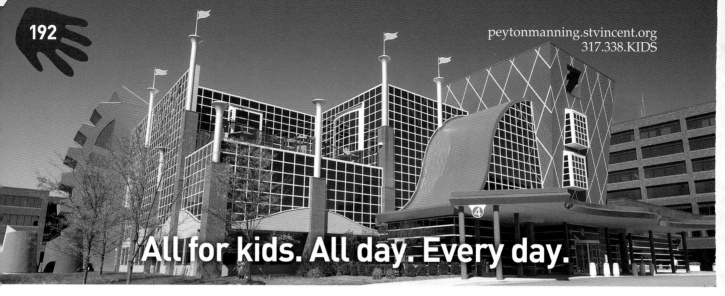